Charles Hendray was born in London between the two world wars, and was educated there. He spent a successful working life as a quantity surveyor, including many years specialising in the resolution of construction disputes.

HEY DIDDLE DIDDLE
An Inside View of the Construction Industry

Charles Hendray

Book Guild Publishing
Sussex, England

First published in Great Britain in 2008 by
The Book Guild Ltd
Pavilion View
19 New Road
Brighton
BN1 1UF

Typesetting in Baskerville by
IML Typographers, Merseyside

Printed in Great Britain by
Athenæum Press Ltd, Gateshead

A catalogue record for this book is available from
The British Library.

ISBN 978 1 84624 202 1

To Brenda,
my loving and patient wife

Contents

Introduction

The usual disclaimers that events recounted are fictitious and that the characters portrayed bear no relation to any real person, living or dead, do not apply to this book. All the events have actually taken place – indeed, I was involved in most of them.

All the characters are real. Many of them are, I hope, still alive. I have changed all their names but, if any of them recognise themselves, I hope they will accept that I have related the truth and not been unkind to them.

I have not augmented or exaggerated the truth even where I know the characters have departed this mortal coil. Doubtless, if they were still around, they would certainly think me somewhat unkind to allude to their shortcomings.

*

'Hey Diddle Diddle', apart from being the name of a very old nursery rhyme, is cockney rhyming slang for 'on the fiddle', that is, operating a scam.

1

True or Imaginary

I have seen a short film entitled *A Home of Your Own* at least four or five times, although it must be over thirty years since I saw it first. I believe it was originally intended to be a humorous, semi-documentary about a young married couple purchasing a new house. As I understand it, it was usual at the end of each day's filming for 'rushes' – rapid prints – to be produced, so that the makers could quickly assess the results of their efforts. Nowadays, with the advent of instant TV replays, the process is probably speeded up.

However, at that time it was usual to view the uncut rushes with no sound track attached. Apparently, the technicians seeing the rushes fell about laughing to such an extent that it was decided to distribute the film without dialogue and simply with sound effects. Many of the actors. barely known at that time, later became stars. I remember particularly Ronnie Barker and Peter Butterworth, both now sadly departed, and Richard Briers. The film depicted numerous comical happenings. To someone unconnected with the Building Industry the events would appear imaginary and staged just for the film. However, I can assure you that for virtually every event depicted in that film I have seen one like it, or very similar to it, enacted in real life. The events that I am relating in this book are – except when I might specifically indicate otherwise – events from my personal recollection. They are all true. I accept that the layman may well find them difficult to believe but, you know truth is sometimes stranger than fiction.

When you look at and admire a finished building you would need to be a part of the Construction Industry to appreciate the complex problems involved in coordinating all the various trades and components. It may seem surprising, but even overcoming the first problem of getting the building in the right place is not as simple as it sounds. I shall say more on this later. Likewise, locating the various components correctly in relation to one another. Reading an account of a completed project in a technical journal fails to give an insight into the undoubted stress and heart-searching that would have been involved.

That stress and heart-searching is chiefly borne on the site by the Contractor's management team. Basically this comprises a Manager at the top. He might simply be known as the Site Manager, however, more usually he is referred to as the Site Agent. He may have one or more Sub-agents working under him. On a very large project he may rejoice in the title of Project Manager and have Agents and Sub-agents working under him. There would be other technical staff such as Engineers – civil or structural – a General Foreman, Section Foremen, various trades Foremen, gangers and so on; the numbers would depend on the size of the project.

There would also be a Quantity Surveyor – my profession. On a large job he would be resident on site and perhaps have several assistants; his title would be Site QS or more grandiosely Project QS. On a smaller job he would simply visit the site periodically.

The Quantity Surveyor is primarily concerned with money. That is to say valuing the work which may involve measuring it, pricing it, calculating the profit or loss that has been made, or forecasting the cash that might be required to carry out, for example, the next three months' work.

Nowadays the Quantity Surveyor is often an integral part of the Management team, having a vital say in deciding how work

2

should be carried out within a specified budget. You may be surprised to learn that even today this is not always the case; and in the past was very rarely the case. The Quantity Surveyor was not encouraged to take any part in the process of site management; indeed he was positively discouraged. I personally succeeded – but only with great difficulty – in spending a part of my career with Contractors as a Site Agent.

The Quantity Surveyors I have described above are the *Contractors'* Quantity Surveyors. They are on one side of the fence. There is another breed on the other side. They are generally referred to as the PQS – the Professional Quantity Surveyors. They act for, and are paid by, the Client – the Building Owner. Notionally they are supposed to be impartial, holding a balance between the Client and the Contractor. Some achieve this, some do not. In either case, they generally have to deal with the Contractor's Surveyor and agree measurements, quantities and prices with him. Since nowadays, more than ever, money is all-important they are 'at the sharp end' and can be veritable gladiators in their own sphere.

The Contractor's Quantity Surveyor, in addition to dealing and negotiating with the Client's Surveyor, also has to deal with Subcontractors who also might employ their own Surveyors. The sums of money involved in construction are so large that most contracts provide for the Contractor to be paid at intervals – generally monthly, but sometimes fortnightly. The PQS will normally recommend or certify the amount of money due to the Contractor at any particular time. Similarly the Contractor's Surveyor will normally authorise the interim payments to be made to Subcontractors. Obviously this carries with it a heavy responsibility and requires the very highest degree of professionalism, honesty and integrity.

All of this sounds very profound, and of course it is; the whole business is very serious. The Main Contractor may price a project to make a gross profit of only 3 per cent; in times of recession, even less. The slightest hiccough can make inroads into it very easily. And hiccoughs there are aplenty; and not just slight ones as I shall relate.

Fortunately it is not just love that makes the world go round – although as I shall also relate, that helps – but laughter as well. Without a sense of humour many members of management teams would probably go mad. A few probably do. More than a few have nervous breakdowns or reach responsible positions and then either ask for, or willingly accept, demotion. I don't know if there are any statistics comparing this sort of thing in the Construction Industry with other Industries but I would guess the stress-failure rates of staff in Construction must be among the highest.

Oddly enough it is often the individuals who, on the face of it, easily stand up to the stress, who suddenly succumb. They are generally the outgoing, extrovert and apparently forceful characters. The quiet, introverted and sometimes worried-looking individuals often have that inner strength, which carries them through. Psychologists would no doubt have the logical explanation; and would surely support the theory that laughter and humour provide the safety valve.

In my own experience times are legion where, at a meeting, which began in an atmosphere of tension and false smiles, the ice was broken by a quiet joke or perhaps some unexpected event which sparked some humour. An accidental slip of the tongue can do it. I remember a very solemn Client moralising at a meeting and proceeding to expound the notion that too many cocks can spoil the broth!

Sometimes the humour is contrived with the occasional practical joke; it evolves out of a perfectly ordinary situation. It may even appear humorous to only one person, whilst being decidedly unfunny to everyone else. Frequently I find that what strikes *me* as funny leaves other people unamused. Perhaps I am the one with the peculiar sense of humour, just like my father. He certainly had a mischievous sense of fun. One of his favourite little japes was to sit in a non-smoking compartment of a train with an unlit cigarette in his mouth and quietly wait for some

4

unsuspecting complainant to point out to him that it was a 'non-smoker'. 'Oh,' he would say with a look of angelic innocence on his face, 'Well, I've got my boots on but I'm not walking!'

On one occasion my father had commented upon a passing female. 'You really have got the most peculiar taste in women,' my mother told him. Everyone fell about laughing – except my mother!

2

What a Sod!

Murphy's Law, or Sod's Law as it's sometimes called, says that if something can go wrong it will; that if it's possible to do something in one of two ways, both of which appear superficially correct but one of which is in fact wrong, the wrong way will be selected, if not every time then significantly more than 50 per cent of the time. This theory was actually disproved on television some years ago when slices of buttered bread were dropped to the ground. According to Sod's Law the slices should have landed buttered side down far more often than not; but it didn't happen.

Nevertheless, I can assure you that if a navvy or a machine excavator is set to work to dig within a metre of a live cable or other service main there is absolutely no doubt at all that the cable or service main will be broken. They positively lurk beneath the ground like an accident waiting to happen. Of course, in the unlikely event of it not happening, nobody gets to know about it and it doesn't enter into the statistics so to speak. But naturally it is the cases where it does happen that stick in the memory.

One such incident that does stick in my memory concerns a site on which a large building was being built. The old buildings, which were on the site, had been demolished. Near the site entrance there was an old bungalow, also scheduled for demolition. However, its demolition was delayed until the latter stages of the job because it was quite useful to the Contractor as one of his site offices.

The time came to demolish the bungalow. As Project Surveyor I agreed a price of £100 with a local demolition firm. That may not sound much money but this was some 40 years ago. In fact, the price may well have been higher than it should have been. Demolition prices can vary considerably according to the credit value of the materials that come out of the demolition, and can also change rapidly according to the local demand at any particular time.

Anyway, the price was agreed and the demolition began. Being a former dwelling house there were obviously utility service mains running to it. Everybody knew they were there, even roughly *where* they were. There shouldn't have been a problem. Even if there was a problem, basically it was the demolition Firm's. They were the experts, used to doing this sort of thing all the time. Insurance-wise, I believe there are strict limits on the liability that such Firms have, because the potential damage they can do is so great that as a matter of public policy they are not liable; certainly not for the sort of damage that occurred on this occasion. Which was rather fortunate from everyone's point of view – except the recipient of the damage, that is.

I was working away diligently – as always! – in my site hut when, following a dainty tap on the door, the Groundwork Foreman came in. 'I suppose I'd better tell you what's happened,' he said.

After that delicate preamble I waited for the worst.

'We've broken the cable into the bungalow.'

'Oh?'

'Well, we haven't actually broken it, we've pulled it.'

'What do you mean you've pulled it?'

'We've pulled it.'

'Pulled it from what?'

'From the main cable under the road.'

'You mean you've knackered the main cable under the road?'

'I suppose so.'

'Oh, shit! Hang on, what do you mean *you've* knackered the

7

cable under the road? We're not doing the work, Joe Bloggs (Demolition) Ltd is doing it.'

'Ah, yes, that's why I thought I'd better tell you what's happened.'

The worst was yet to come!

'Tell me.'

'Well it was actually our machine that pulled the cable.'

'What was our machine doing there?'

'We were giving Bloggsy a hand – *you* know.'

'Go on.'

'Well our machine had a bit of spare time so we were doing the knocking down and Bloggsy's wagons were taking away the rubble – *you* know.'

I did know, or I could guess. Bloggsy was on to a good thing. We – the Main Contractor – by whom the Groundwork Foreman and I were both employed, were paying him £100 to do a job that we were actually doing for him. Except, that is for the carting away of the brick hardcore, timber, leadwork, roof tiles etc., all of which he was selling for more than the cost of the carting. Needless to say, the arrangement was that the Groundwork Foreman could get a 'drink' out of it. I would have remained in total ignorance of the whole thing but for the mishap; and in due course would have innocently authorised the payment of the £100 to Bloggs. Everybody would had been happy. Except the recipient of the damage – the adjoining factory served by the main electricity cable. The production line was halted for four hours whilst the repair was carried out. Even some 40 years ago the cost involved was over £20,000 an hour!

3

The CoW Jumped Over the Moon

The Clerk of Works is an inspector. Generally he is employed by the Architect, sometimes by the Client. Sometimes he is authorised to issue day-to-day site instructions to the Contractor, sometimes not; but essentially he is an inspector. Many Clerks of Works are former tradesmen. Occasionally they are referred to rather derogatorily in the same way as Bernard Shaw spoke of teachers: 'Those who can, do; those who can't, teach.' said Shaw. 'Those who can do; those who can't become Clerks of Works,' say the wags.

On a small job if there is a Clerk of Works at all he will visit the site periodically, perhaps daily, perhaps only two or three times a week. On a large job he will be resident on the site. On a very large job he may have one or more assistants.

A good Clerk of Works can be very helpful to a Contractor. If there is a query in connection with a working drawing he can solve the problem, quickly authorising the Contractor on how to proceed and even getting the Architect out of trouble. He is the man on the spot and he can oil the wheels. He is not there just to find faults with the Contractor's work. If he discovers something wrong he can assist the Contractor to find a way of overcoming the difficulty without necessarily resorting to condemning the work. It is in everyone's interest to get the job finished as expeditiously as possible. Condemning work . which might involve dismantling or demolishing it, causes a delay. Of course, sometimes there may be no alternative. For example, a wall built in the wrong place may *have* to be corrected. However, if the position in which it was built was not critical, it would be churlish to insist on its demolition and reconstruction.

The majority of Clerks of Works are helpful. Apart from anything else they have probably taken the job because it involves much less responsibility than that of a Foreman – a relatively easy life, and being helpful is easier than being a bastard. However, there are those who enjoy being bastards, like the traffic warden who watches you park on a double yellow line and then bangs a ticket on your windscreen. Clerks of Works with a mean streak will watch a wall being built in the wrong place, wait for a few days until it is plastered and then condemn it. Highly bastorial, as they say.

One Clerk of Works I remember used to walk around the site with a copy of the specification under his arm condemning everything that was not absolutely in accordance with it to the letter. A sort of barrack-room lawyer. Eventually the job was being delayed so much the *Client* had him shifted.

George Kay was definitely not in that category. He was a lovely man, kind, helpful, mostly smiling and, when I first came across him, 89 years old! He would walk around the site every day, chatting to everyone, giving advice to anyone who asked and those who didn't. If he saw something wrong he would point it out straight away with more than a hint as to how it could be put right quickly and easily. From the Client's point of view his one fault was perhaps his propensity to sign things a bit too readily, like site instructions or daywork sheets; particularly daywork sheets.

Daywork sheets are records of time and materials allegedly spent on work that the Contractor might consider to be an extra and that, because of its alleged degree of difficulty, cannot be properly related to contract rates. Thus once a daywork sheet is signed by the Clerk of Works it might be difficult for the Client's Quantity Surveyor – the PQS – to insist on the work being

CLERKS OF WORKS (BASTARD TYPE) — EXAMPLES:—

A. Cairo, Egypt — 2400 B.C.

B. Barcelona, Spain — 2400 A.D.

measured and valued at contract rates. Hence, from the Contractor's point of view, it is a good idea to foster an excellent relationship with the Clerk of Works! Friendly dealings on the site will achieve this. The occasional beer and a sandwich or business lunch will help and, provided it is not overdone, does not overstep the bounds of legitimacy. As long as no money passes hands, or there is no other incentive in kind offered or accepted, I believe there can be no complaint.

As far as I know George Kay was surprisingly honest. He was a very popular character. Everyone on site was therefore very sad when one day, when climbing through a window opening to look at a balcony (and by this time he was 92 years old!), he fell 3 to 4 feet and broke his arm. He was taken to hospital and we all thought we had seen the last of him.

But not a bit of it. Four weeks later he was back on site relating the tale of his hospital stay. Apparently there was a very strict Sister in charge of his ward. She goaded him and disciplined him, making him get out of bed to exercise frequently or go to the toilet. She even woke him up, so he said, just to stop him sleeping. His one ambition was that, on the day he was discharged from the hospital, he was going to call that Sister a cow. And he achieved it, as he told us when he arrived back on site, beaming all over his face!

I am sure that wonderful Sister laughed or wept tears of joy at her success in getting his adrenalin flowing to spur him on to recovery.

*

Bill Cotter was in a quite different category. Much younger than George Kay for a start – but then most people were. By all accounts Bill Cotter was the archetypal bastard Clerk of Works. In fact, he was generally referred to as 'that bastard Cotter'. I had heard about him and the aggravation he was causing on a job in the north-west of England long before I was asked to visit the job myself. The likelihood of my having to travel to the North-West

and visit that particular site was remote, but as it happened the job was losing a lot of money. I was dragooned to go up and find out why.

When I arrived I found that Cotter's name seemed to encroach into almost every conversation. He reputedly suffered from every possible virtue: he was virtuous, religious and often monopolised conversations with his moralising. He certainly did not have George Kay's affinity for signing his autograph; he wouldn't sign anything if he could possibly avoid it.

But he did like the sound of his own voice. One afternoon a meeting was arranged for me to attend at which Bill Cotter was present. We were introduced and he began chatting and regaling us with some anecdotes from his past.

'... and they said to me, Gillie – they used to call me Gillie in those days after the comedian Gillie Potter because I was known as Billy Cotter and it rhymed – Gillie they said ...'

At that moment I realised that I had met him before when he was a General Foreman on a job where I worked as a junior assistant Surveyor. 'Christ we've met before,' I said, 'you were on a job in London docks twenty years ago.'

'That's right, but I don't remember you.'

'Well I wasn't long out of school then, but I remember you, you were knocking-off the site typist Mrs Wilkinson. Her husband was away in the forces.'

It just came straight out without a thought. There was a few seconds' stunned silence then everyone – except Cotter – burst out laughing. Cotter went absolutely scarlet. At that moment I think he could easily have killed me.

The general comment to me afterwards was on the lines of, 'Well at least the bastard's human after all!' But I never met him again to find out.

4

We'll Have to Stop Meeting Like This

Site meetings are an important part of any construction project. Sometimes they are called progress meetings simply because they are generally held at regular intervals throughout the progress of the job. The idea is to try to overcome any problems that may have arisen and to coordinate the activities of the whole of the Construction Team.

The meetings are normally chaired by the Contract Administrator. This is the person designated in the Contract to 'supervise' the works. He – or she – doesn't supervise the individual workmen or, generally, even decide how the job should be carried out. He is a professional appointed by the Building Owner to supervise the project, hopefully to ensure that it is completed on time and in accordance with the specification. On a Building contract he would, in most cases, be an Architect, but he could be the Quantity Surveyor or, on a large scheme, a person appointed by name as a Project Manager or Contract Administrator. On a Civil Engineering contract he would probably be a Civil Engineer.

In most cases the meetings are held at fortnightly intervals. You would think that organising them would be straightforward enough; but not necessarily so. In the first place it has to be decided who is going to attend and who is not. Obviously the Architect – the designer of the job – must attend or be represented. He may or may not want the Professional Quantity Surveyor to be there.

15

In the early structural stages of the job the Structural Engineer would attend. The Main Contractor's Site Agent or Manager would also be present. He may or may not want his General Foreman or *his* Quantity Surveyor to attend. Perhaps, more significantly, he may or may not want any of the Subcontractors to be represented. There is an important reason behind this. The meetings are held, as I have said, to overcome problems; in practice, often to establish who has actually caused the problems. On all too frequent occasions there may be recriminations followed by financial charges being levied on the alleged culprit. An astute Main Contractor will try to avoid his Subcontractors being present to hear him being blamed for some error or failure of coordination. By holding a separate Subcontractors' meeting he can avoid this. He can also avoid the possibility of the Contract Administrator hearing Subcontractors blaming the Main Contractor or each other.

The meetings are usually minuted. Minutes of site meetings are, generally speaking, not strictly 'minutes', that is to say just records of decisions taken. In most cases, they become a semi-verbatim record of the discussions. Certainly at some later date if, unfortunately, there is a dispute involving legal proceedings, the site meeting minutes or notes may become very significant.

So, in the second place it has to be decided who will prepare the minutes. The 'norm' would be the Chairman, that is probably the Contract Administrator. However, it is very much a chore that – once again – an astute Contractor can play to his advantage. He will generously volunteer to prepare the minutes, which in the usual way will come up for approval at the following meeting. The minutes, worded very carefully, will delicately understate items for which 'blame' might be attributed to the Contractor at a later date, whilst at the same time giving rather more emphasis than they merit to items that might later benefit the Contractor. An unwitting Contract Administrator could find himself in considerable trouble in times to come if he is not very careful.

This is not to say that slanting or bias in the recorded minutes is the sole prerogative of Contractors. Many 'professional' Architects and Contract Administrators are equally adept at it, with broadly similar aims. For example, they will understate any delay that might have occurred as a result of a failure to give the Contractor working information by the due time, at the same time placing emphasis on any shortcomings on the Contractor's part that may have been revealed.

This little preliminary game of chess proceeds unsung, sometimes unbeknown or even unsuspected by the principal parties involved, at the time when the first meeting has barely got under way.

I have found over the years that at business meetings generally 90 per cent of the talking is done by about 20 per cent of those attending. And so it is at most site meetings. Most of the talking is done by the Chairman and the senior person representing the Contractor. As Quantity Surveyor I generally found I needed to say very little. Only when I was personally in the chair have I found it necessary to do a lot of the talking. I was given two very pertinent pieces of advice quite early in my career appertaining to attendance at meetings:

1.   Better to remain silent and let people think you are a fool, than to speak and make 'em certain!
2.   Hear all, see all, say **** all!

5

Although Meeting Like this Can be Quite ...

I remember one site meeting held on a site at a university in the Midlands. The job was nearly finished and I had had nothing to do with it previously. I was representing the Quantity Surveyor appointed by the university – the PQS – whose previous representative had departed for pastures new. I knew very little about the job except that it had been running behind programme and was over budget. Thus, neither the Contractor nor the Architect, nor indeed the PQS, were exactly popular with the employing Authority who – in the person of the University Bursar – was also attending the meeting. In fact the Bursar had been in the habit of attending most of the previous meetings, which were held in his conference room.

The meeting duly commenced and proceeded with numerous recriminations resulting from the various problems. I was lumbered with some awkward questions to which I did not know all the answers. And even when I did know the answers I judged it expedient not to be explicit. So I was quite relieved when it was suggested that tea and biscuits would be served shortly.

It is often a relief to break for a 'cuppa' during a site meeting even when the quality of the tea leaves much to be desired. However, on this occasion I felt there was more than just a feeling of relief around the table when the Bursar picked up the phone and said, 'Susan, we're ready for tea now.' I believe someone muttered something like, 'Yes, God bless Susan.' I was soon to find out why.

Apparently the routine was quite well established; only being the first occasion on which I had attended this particular series of meetings, I was blissfully unaware of it. Susan appeared carrying a tray of cups of tea, which she placed on a side table. She then proceeded to go round the table placing a cup in front of each person whilst the business of the meeting had come to a halt.

Susan was a good-looking girl. In particular she was wearing a very attractive low-cut dress, which enclosed – or at least partially enclosed – a stupendous pair of 38 double-D's. As she went along the other side of the table placing the teacups, she leaned over deliciously between each person. On my side of the table eyes popped, whilst on the other side angelic smiles prevailed as each individual's face came in close proximity. I observed that several times actual contact was made. My eager anticipation was rewarded when my cup was placed in front of me and one half of the 38 double-D twins delicately and softly brushed my cheek. Bliss! Self-restraint was the order of the day whilst eyes now popped on the other side of the table.

Somehow, when the meeting got under way again, the recriminations seemed less purposeful and a more friendly atmosphere prevailed! Or possibly I wasn't fully paying attention. Mind you, my view of University Bursars was never quite the same again.

*

Whilst the tea interval is always welcome at a site meeting it does present certain hazards (apart from the likes of the lovely Susan, I mean). Invariably the meeting table is covered with papers, files and a multitude of drawings, and nothing is worse than tea-stained drawings or correspondence. I have a horror of upsetting tea over drawings or documents. Unfortunately the tea is only rarely served by the likes of Susan. More usually a tea man or boy is designated to serve it in half-pint mugs, and only rarely are those placed on the meeting table without either spilling some of the contents or leaving circular imprints on the papers.

I managed to hit the jackpot at one meeting. The tea man had delivered the mugs of tea. Unnoticed by me, he had placed my mug on the corner of my writing pad. As I lifted the pad I up-ended the mug. As the tea flowed over the table towards my neighbour he jumped, upset his own tea, jogged the fellow next to him who did likewise and so on. Six or seven mugs were upset. The table was swimming in tea. The Architect Chairman – not renowned for his sense of humour – just said in a droll voice, 'Well, if the Contractor's staff are going to start tipping tea over each other we'd better adjourn.'

*

Another meeting on the same job sticks in my memory. The project was the construction of a workshop and office building. The workshop section was quite large and comprised two storeys. Much of the equipment to be installed required the use of compressed air. Thus, in addition to the usual electricity, water and gas services, there was a network of compressed air pipes. The main pipeline ran from corner to corner of the building. The compressor was located outside the building and the main 150 mm (6″) diameter line entered the building just below ceiling level at one corner and ran to the diagonally opposite corner where it turned upwards to provide a compressed air service to the first floor.

The structural first floor, that is the ground-floor ceiling, was 150–200 mm (6″–8″) thick. A hole was required in the corner for the compressed air main to pass through. Such holes are sometimes formed when the concrete is poured by leaving a box or mould in it. It is surprisingly difficult to ensure that such boxes are left in the right place. Even if they are placed correctly, they can easily be moved during the pouring of the concrete. In any case, they may simply be overlooked and not placed at all. Either way the result can be that there is no hole where there should be one, and a hole has to be cut.

Ensuring that a hole is cut in the right place is easier than ensuring that it is formed in the right place. The actual cutting can present a problem however. Cutting the concrete is not necessarily a problem if the right tools are used, but the concrete is reinforced with steel rods and Murphy/ Sod's Law decrees that wherever you want to cut a hole there will be some. These must not be cut or moved without the permission of the Structural Engineer responsible for the design.

In this particular instance the specialist Firm installing the compressed air pipelines had run the 150 mm diameter main from its entry point at one corner of the building to the point at the opposite corner where it was supposed to turn upwards into the first floor. No hole had been left in the floor slab and their Foreman – a Hungarian fellow – had asked for one to be cut.

The days and weeks passed. The Hungarian Foreman badgered the Main Contractor's staff to get the hole cut. It reached the stage when every morning he arrived on the site the first thing he did was to visit the corner of the building to see if it had materialised since the previous afternoon.

The poor chap related this sorry saga when it came to his turn to speak at a site meeting. In his broken English he told how he had chased the Section Foreman, the General Foreman, the Engineers and finally the Project Manager, to get the hole cut. 'Yesterday morning, he said 'I came in and finally ze hole was zere. I vent to my store to get ze bend to fix through ze floor but ven I got back to ze corner ze *Plumber* had put his soil pipe through my hole! I ask *everyone*, but no vun vill tell me vot I must do viz my pipe!'

There was about five seconds silence before somebody made a rather impractical suggestion.

22

6

Magic Moments

Before I started my own surveying practice I had worked for just five different Firms. Thus I changed jobs only four times, three times entirely of my own volition, once 'by mutual consent'. I did not go for many interviews in the early stages of my career; it was an era of full employment.

The first two moves were motivated by a desire for a change of scenery. On the first occasion I advertised my services in a trade journal. The current necessity, in today's economic climate, to write dozens of letters each accompanied by a CV was unknown then. I advertised in the 'services offered' column and received telegrams in response from prospective Employers 100 miles apart. Numerous others responded by post. At the interviews it was generally the Employers who were trying to make themselves attractive. I have never felt that I came over well in these situations. At that time it probably did not matter; most Employers made an offer there and then.

One chap who did not impress me in the way he might have intended, had a very large office. The entrance door was at one end whilst his desk – on a raised dais – was at the other. After keeping me waiting, his secretary ushered me in and I had what seemed like an interminable walk to approach him. He invited me to be seated in a rather low chair from which I could look up at him at an angle of 30 or 40 degrees. He clearly wanted me to regard him as God. Since I did not regard myself as an angel, I decided not to risk a clash of personalities. At one of the interviews I have already mentioned, the Manager actually interviewed me with his feet on the table. Nevertheless, he was a discerning fellow, since he offered me a job, albeit on a month's trial.

On each of the later occasions I looked for a change I did not advertise my services, or indeed respond to any Employer's advertisement. I simply wrote 'on spec' to a large Firm. Each time I was called for an interview and offered a position that I accepted.

The idea of a month's trial is not a bad one. Many people who, like myself, do not impress at interviews for one reason or another, then get the opportunity to prove themselves in practice over a period of weeks. This can benefit both Employer and Employee alike. Some people can be quite impressive at interviews but when it comes to actually doing the job they fall down.

In some ways an interviewee is like a witness giving evidence in court before a Judge or Arbitrator. The one who speaks clearly and incisively and looks you straight in the eye whilst giving evidence is not necessarily the one who is telling the truth or who is the most capable. Conversely, the one who tends to waffle on a bit and appears shifty is not necessarily lying. The fact that he may well be more knowledgeable and more truthful than the other chap simply hidden by more nerves!

On the final occasion I 'changed jobs' it was not of my own volition or by mutual consent. After being offered two or three transfers to other positions, which I regarded either as demotions or steps sideways, I was made redundant. Being made redundant was not as commonplace then as it is now. I found it quite soul-destroying.

I certainly got plenty of practice at being interviewed then. Over the period of my three months' notice I attended some eighty interviews, all of which were unsuccessful. I had never been out of work before and the day that I had to register as unemployed was something of a nightmare – definitely not a magic moment.

Interviewee's-eye view – 'I'll give you a month's trial, OK?'

25

However, my luck was in because within a day or so I obtained some part-time work on a self-employed basis. Thus was my small Surveying practice born.

The part-time work comprised working or 'charring' for another surveying Firm. There were five members of staff, including myself and a telephonist/secretary all working in one large room. When the telephonist/secretary decided she wanted to depart, the Firm advertised for a replacement. On the appointed day a Partner came from the Head Office to do the interviews. During the interviews, those of us who were also in the same room carried on working – or at least gave all the appearance of so doing. Each of the interviews lasted fifteen or twenty minutes, and were set at half-hourly intervals to provide for a short break between.

One of the interviews sticks in my mind as a classic. There was a delicate tap on the door and in walked a beautiful girl about 6′ tall, bedecked in a fur wrap sufficiently low-cut to vie with the ultra-short miniskirt she was wearing, which in turn revealed a superb pair of legs complete with high heels. We all held our breath as she sidled across the room, greeted the Partner, seated herself on the chair in front of him and delicately crossed her legs. Then she uncrossed them and recrossed them.

I don't think the Partner knew where to look. He asked all the usual questions but whether or not he heard the answers I don't know. As soon as she had gone he pronounced that 'no way would she get the job'. Notwithstanding that according to her CV, she was quite suited to it – and in spite of the fact that we were unanimous in our view that she was most definitely the one who should be offered the position!

*

The 80-odd interviews I attended in my own search for a job were quite interesting in retrospect, although demoralising at the time. I was successful in none of them, although I was compelled to apply for many positions well below my capability and junior in status to the position from which I had been made redundant. As I say, being made redundant was not as commonplace at that time as it is nowadays. When I told an interviewer that my reason for changing my job was redundancy I felt I was not believed. After all, Firms do not make their best staff redundant. Of course, I could have lied about it, as in effect I did in the early interviews by not disclosing that I had been made redundant. But in the latter stages, when I was getting desperate, I needed to say that I was available at short notice.

But it was all to no avail. For the most part I was too capable for the jobs I was going for. I might have done better to have down-graded my ability. I could almost hear the interviewers thinking 'I don't want him – he could do my job.'

7

To See Such Fun

Much of the work carried out on a construction site has to be measured and valued after it is done. 'Valuing' is perhaps a slightly misleading term in this context because, in most cases, the basis of pricing the work has previously been agreed. Whilst a certain amount of assessment or negotiation may be required in some circumstances, the detailed unit rates, that is the rates per cubic metre, square metre etc. are those embodied in the Contractor's – or Subcontractor's – tender.

Except where work is priced on a 'lump sum' basis – that is a total sum of money for a fixed amount of work, for example the installation of three passenger lifts – tenders generally used to take the form of prices appended to items listed in Bills of Quantities. The Bills were prepared by the Professional Quantity Surveying Firm (the PQS) and listed – hopefully – all the myriad items of work in the various trades which went to make up the completed project.

On many projects the quantities listed in the Bills were firm and final. They would only be amended in the event of variations or – heaven forbid – an error being found in them. On these projects, the quantities were said to 'form part of the contract'. However, there could be certain sections of the work that were not fully designed at tender stage or which, for some other reason, it was not possible to prepare firm quantities. In those cases approximate quantities would be included in the Bills and the work would be

28

remeasured 'as executed' after it was completed. The quantities included were then described as 'provisional'.

On some projects, in order to get tendering under way and work commenced quickly, Bills of Approximate Quantities or schedules of works without any quantities listed, are prepared. In those cases the whole of the works will have to be remeasured as they are completed. Quantities listed at tender stage would not then form part of the contract.

Most Contractors sublet a large proportion of their contracts these days. In theory, on a contract where the Quantities 'form a part' it should not be necessary to remeasure the work except, as I say, to adjust for variations or errors. In practice most subcontract works are remeasured. There are a number of reasons for this.

Firstly, it enables the Main Contractor to check the quantities listed in the Bills. Of course it ought not to be necessary to actually measure the work on site in order to do this. The Contractor's Surveyor could 'take-off' the quantities from the drawing. Even better, the PQS could provide the Contractor with a copy of his original take-off dimensions. You may not be surprised to find that PQS's are peculiarly reluctant to do this. Presumably they assume – possibly correctly – that the Contractor's Surveyor will immediately sit down and go through the dimensions with a fine tooth comb with the object of pointing out omissions, whilst at the same time conveniently overlooking any duplications. Be that as it may, it is rare indeed for a Contractor to even have sight of the PQS's original dimensions, let alone be given a copy of them.

Secondly, there is an innate distrust amongst Subcontractors of measurements prepared from drawings. Each following trade would have to assume that each preceding trade has accurately built what is shown on the drawings. Finishing trades in particular have no confidence that this would be the case. Their distrust is frequently well justified, as I shall show in due course.

There is yet another reason why Subcontract works are remeasured, the ethics of which are decidedly dubious. For example, if for every 100 square metres of plastering the Contractor can measure and pay the Subcontractor for only 98 square metres, whilst at the same time obtaining payment for 102 square metres himself, a significant extra profit can be made. The difference may seem minimal but it has to be compared with the gross profit margin of the Contractor, which may well be less than 5 per cent on his costs.

In one sense there is nothing unethical about all this. After all, all the parties involved are, or should be, capable of looking after themselves. They can fight their corner. But is it really worth the trouble of having to measure whole trades twice? I have never thought so although I have done it on numerous occasions. The primary problem I had as the Contractor's Surveyor was at least to ensure that I did not pay a Subcontractor for larger quantities than my Employer was being paid for. I often tried to persuade Subcontractors to accept payment on the basis of the same quantities the Contractor was being paid for, but this was only realistically possible if the work was being remeasured for the Main Contractor trade-by-trade. Often remeasurement for the Main Contractor would combine two or more trades, for example, plasterers and decorating, at the same time; and to remeasure several different Subcontractors' work simultaneously was simply not practicable.

You may wonder how it is possible to measure 100 square metres of work and make it come to 98 on one day and 102 on another; I can assure you it can be done. Absolute strict appliance of the rules of measurement on one day, with a less rigid appliance on the next, coupled with perhaps a small difference in wall heights on each occasion, will amount to a surprising difference in the two sets of measurements.

On one large refurbishment job, which required the whole interior of the building to be gutted on each floor, the new floor finish was expensive, hardwood strip boarding. I fully intended to pay the Subcontractor for the same quantities as my Firm was being paid. I got on well with the PQS and we had agreed quite generous measurements with him. However the Managing Director of the flooring firm had come on site and 'ordered' me to measure the work with his Surveyor on a particular day. It was not convenient for me and he complained to one of my Firm's Directors, with whom he was friendly. He complained to my Chief. There was aggravation all down the line.

The subbie's Managing Director was not popular on the site anyway. He had adopted a similar attitude with the Project Manager as he had with me. He was quite obnoxious at site meetings; he never stopped talking – he was the classic sufferer from oral diarrhoea.

'Right,' we said, 'we'll have him! The measuring tape had never been pulled so tight! Every column, every small wall projection was deducted. The strip flooring passed under all the lightweight partitions since, for speed, the flooring had been laid first. We measured all the rooms 'nett', effectively deducting out all the partitions. We knew we had gained well in the measurements, and yet when we compared the two sets of measurements the difference was far greater than we had expected. How could we have done so well? We investigated; what we found took us by surprise.

There were two floors of identical layout. We had measured one and doubled up the dimensions for the other. However, on the floor we measured there was one very large room that contained a lot of telephone and other equipment. The floor was finished in vinyl tiling not hardwood strip. On the floor we did not measure the corresponding room *was* finished in hardwood strip. Quite inadvertently we had forgotten to add it in.

In the normal course of events we would have corrected such an error. In this case we just said 'Sod him!'. Amazingly the omission was apparently never noticed.

*

Plumbing is one trade that frequently has to be remeasured after it is complete. It is theoretically possible to take-off pipework from drawings, but only on rare occasions is the design of the installation sufficiently far advanced when the Bills of Quantities are prepared to enable this to be done accurately. Additionally, it may well be left to the plumber to decide the best route for his pipework. Thus, when the work is measured it is essential for the Plumber's Supervisor or the Foreman Plumber to accompany the Surveyors to explain where all the pipe runs and associated work are.

Obviously it is not practicable or desirable to measure the work twice. Sometimes the PQS will say to the Contractor's Surveyor, 'You measure it with the Plumber and give me a copy of the dimensions and I'll spot-check them.' Whether or not he does spot-check them, in the event he saves himself a lot of work – for which, of course, he is getting paid a fee – and so everyone is happy. This might be categorised as a 'professional fiddle' because the Client, who is actually paying the fee, does not know about the arrangement.

Sometimes the PQS is more diligent and insists on being present when the work is measured. There will then be three or probably four people in the party going round the site doing the measuring – the PQS, the Contractor's Surveyor, the Sub-contractor's Surveyor, the Plumbing Supervisor (although he may also double as the Surveyor) and possibly the Foreman Plumber. Often the work can only be measured when everything is complete and the building is occupied and in use. This will involve entering toilet areas, which may cause the occasional minor problem, particularly if one of the party is female, as is increasingly the case these days.

On one large project some years ago there were four of us – all male – in the party carrying out the measurements. In one area of the building there were two large sets of toilets – one male, one female. Between the two there was a service duct about 1·25 metres (four feet or so) in width. All the pipework, ventilation ducting and much of the electrical wiring was located in the service duct.

In the toilet areas themselves, the cubicles backed on to the service duct. This was so that the flushing cisterns and pipework serving the toilets could be installed in it, meaning that much cheaper cisterns could be utilised and a more economical scheme of pipework could be followed. All that was visible in the cubicles were the handles or pads necessary to operate the flushing mechanisms. Turning the handles or pressing the pads operated a system of levers through the partition wall and into the service duct to the flushing cistern.

The service duct was fitted with lights and, once inside, we could shut the entrance door and be concealed from the inquisitive eyes of the building occupants. And, of course, from inside we could hear the occupants putting the toilets to good use. In particular from the female side we could hear the pitter-patter of stiletto heels on the hard tile floor. With a little practice we could divine which particular cubicles were being used. And from where we were we could operate the flushing mechanisms to the cisterns. Pitter-patter of high heels; slam! as the door shut; thud! as the bolt shot home; rustle, rustle; delicate plomp as a little bottom hit the seat. Give it about five seconds and pull the lever. The reaction varied from squeals to hysterical laughter.

We tried it a few times on the male side too. No squeals or laughter there, just a fairly consistent, 'What the ****ing hell's going on?'

Speaking of Plumbing Supervisors who also double as Surveyors (or vice versa) reminds me of one job when the Supervisor was not only the Surveyor, but he had also priced the job in the first place. In addition he also organised the labour and ordered all the materials. The job made a loss! The poor chap had nowhere to go – but out!

8

Hey Diddle Diddle – Who's on the Fiddle?

The vast majority of people are honest. A small minority are seriously dishonest. But for quite a sizeable proportion there is a sort of 'thrill of the chase' in obtaining something in a slightly underhand, clandestine or dishonest fashion. As a cockney would say, it's more fun on the hey diddle diddle.

There are the very minor fiddles, so commonplace they are virtually accepted as normal and don't even rate a dishonest category, like making personal calls on the office phone. They start with a quick local call, then the calls get longer in both time and distance. And the time is not just the time and cost of the call. Very often the productive time lost by the person involved is infinitely more than the cost of the call. Using office equipment, like pens, envelopes or the office photocopier, is another minor fiddle.

Inflating expenses is a standard norm for some people. When I was a junior Surveyor I worked under a fellow who had refined it to an art. Under his 'tuition' I became quite adept myself. On one occasion I was commissioned by the Firm's Chief Estimator to travel on the overnight train from London to Merthyr Tydfil in South Wales to deliver a tender by 9.30 the following morning. Time was so short I had to complete some of the figures on the journey. When I returned I duly compiled a stupendous petty cash bill: breakfast, lunch, taxis, gratuities, you name it, it was there. I gave it to the Chief Estimator with some trepidation. He looked at it for about thirty seconds. 'Hm, don't blame you,' he said, and signed it. The 'profit' was equal to about three weeks' wages.

I remember a senior Engineer on one large job I was on getting the hump one month. A diplomatic question elicited the explanation that his expenses had not exceeded his salary that month. He had actually had to draw on his wages to give his wife some housekeeping money!

The trouble with fiddles is that they are like Topsy – they tend to grow and grow. What is arguably 'acceptable' and what is downright dishonest, perhaps even criminal, becomes blurred. Some fiddles start by accident. An innocent mistake that results in there being too much money in the petty cash box; no one notices, and the thought is born that it could be repeated, and perhaps on a larger scale.

Subcontractors on construction sites like to foster good relations with the Main Contractor's staff. A beer and a sandwich helps to oil the wheels. An occasional slap-up lunch. Then perhaps a slap-up lunch every Friday. Then one Friday the subbie's representative tells the Contractor's Foreman he's 'a bit tied up today but look here's a few quid, have a lunch on us anyway'. It is a short step for the few quid to become a regular habit and the Foreman or Site Agent is under an obligation to the Subcontractor; an obligation easily discharged when the subbie wants a chitty signed to authorise payment for something or other. And the beauty – or depending on how you look at it, the horror of it – is that as long as no one gets too greedy, this sort of fiddle is virtually undetectable. So much so that in some Firms a blind eye is turned to a certain amount of fiddling. As long as greed does not take over and the staff concerned otherwise do a good job, the minor fiddles are accepted as legitimate 'perks' by both the Firm and the staff concerned.

I personally don't agree with this and without wishing to sound 'holier than thou' can honestly say that I have never accepted anything more than the occasional lunch or small gift at Christmas. However, from time to time, I have been aware of others on the 'hey diddle diddle' both minor and major. As I have said, the vast majority of people are honest. However, notwithstanding the number of fiddles that I knew of when I was a mere employee, I have since become convinced that I was absolutely naive. Far more went on than I would have believed. It was not until I became self-employed and had Subcontractor Clients that I found a whole different world existed.

I had thought myself a good judge of character. It was not the people I had suspected of being dishonest who created the surprises. It was the ones who I had thought were scrupulously honest and who turned out to be 'bent', who shattered my illusions.

One such 'bent' individual was a member of the buying department of a large Firm I had worked for. He had been there some thirty years when I left for pastures new. Some years later, running my own business, I had occasion to attend a meeting with him in the company of a Subcontractor Client on whose behalf I had prepared a tender.

The meeting went well enough and I emerged feeling quite pleased that we stood a good chance of obtaining the order for the subcontract work, particularly because this was, at least in some part, due to my previous acquaintance with the buyer.

When we got outside my Client said to me, 'He's on the make.'

'What?'

'He's on the take.'

'How do you mean?'

'He's looking for a backhander.'

'Never! He's as honest as the day is long. He's been there over thirty years. Anyway, what makes you think he's looking for a bribe?'

'Didn't you notice how the conversation kept on coming back to how expensive things are these days?'

'Yes, but so what, just polite conversation.'

'Not likely, he mentioned the price of holidays two or three times.'

'No, you are imagining it.'

Nevertheless a couple of weeks later my Client announced to

me that he had got the order for the job. Apparently he had taken the buyer out to lunch that day, after which they had called into a travel agent!

*

Looking back, perhaps I should have been wise to the sort of technique used by the buyer. When I left the Firm he was with I joined another large Company and at various times I worked with three different regions. With one region I was Project Surveyor on an extensive job where there were a large number of Sub-contractors. As it happened, only one ever offered me a 'commission' on his payments. Perhaps the large flea in his ear I dispatched him with deterred any others. However, there were some good Subcontractors who regularly worked for the Firm on a series of contracts, solely because – as I first thought – they gave good service.

They did give good service and it was quite legitimate that they should get follow-up orders as a result. By good service I mean they got the job done whether or not the Main Contractor held them up. In other words they could, and frequently did, get the Main Contractor and his staff out of trouble. Of course, quite reasonably there was a tacit understanding that the Subcontractor would be reimbursed for any undue expense he incurred, for example, in putting right a mistake made by the Main Contractor. Frequently I had to assess that 'undue expense' and, had I been so inclined, could have made myself a few dishonest pounds out of it.

One particular Subcontractor supplied bricklaying gangs on a labour-only basis. That is, the Main Contractor provided all the bricks, mortar, scaffolding and so on. The subbie provided only the bricklayers and the labourers attending them. He was one of the most likeable chaps I have ever met. From time to time he took me out to lunch and he absolutely beamed bonhomie with his genial, round, smiling face. Sadly, he was only fifty years old when he suddenly had a fatal heart attack.

Before that happened he had told me a few stories about my

own departmental Chief. At the time I was quite sceptical as to the truth of them – after all my Chief was a Quantity Surveyor! – but subsequently I found out from various sources that the stories were all too true. Amongst the various tales he told me was that my Chief – I'll call him Ned F. – always made a point of suggesting lunch near Regent Street in central London if he was 'in need'. This made it quite convenient to call into a travel agent or to admire the men's suits in the windows of Austin Reed.

At one point Ned F. was in the process of building himself a large new house. My subbie did the brickwork. 'Don't worry,' he said to me. 'You haven't got to pay me for it on your job because I'm being paid for it on another one.'

'That's just as well then because I wouldn't pay you on my job.'

'You would if Ned said so.'

'Oh no I bloody well wouldn't.'

The phrase 'pay for it' actually did not mean that I wrote out the cheque. It meant that I filled in a printed certificate form and signed it, thereby certifying that the monies stated were due and should be paid to the Subcontractor. The certificate was sent to the accounts department, where the cheque was prepared, The funny thing was that if the amount certified was in excess of £5,000, the certificate had to be sent to Ned F. or his deputy to be counter-signed. This was supposedly as a safeguard against me being on the fiddle! In reality it was no safeguard at all because there was virtually no way anybody at Head Office or Regional Office could verify an amount certified by a Project Surveyor. Later, when I had been promoted and had to do the countersigning, I never felt entirely happy about it.

Ned or his deputy sometimes 'went through the motions'. If I certified a five- or six-figure sum as due to a Subcontractor one or the other would telephone me. 'That £80,000 you've certified for so-and-so is it right?

'Of course it's bloody well right.'

'It's a large amount of money.'

'They've done a lot of work.'

'All right then.'

Ned F.'s house, however, had ramifications for me beyond the brickwork. There was some ornate joinery on my job; also in Ned's house – and the same Firm apparently manufactured both.

One day the Managing Director of the joinery Firm telephoned me. 'I've made some lovely doors and a beautiful staircase, for Mr F.'s new house. Do I send the invoice to you?'

'It's nothing to do with me.'

'I thought you were going to pay for them on your job.'

'No.'

'Well, where do I send the invoice then?'

'Send it to Mr F.'

'Oh I can't do that!'

I rather suspect the joinery Firm never got paid for Ned F.'s staircase and doors.

Every now and then I would get a phone call from Ned F. telling me to 'pay some extra money this month to your painter'.

'What for?'

'One of the directors has had his house painted.'

At first I believed it, but later I suspected the extra money was for work on Ned F.'s house. Either way, there was no problem in dealing with it at the interim payment stages. The amounts I was certifying for the painter were so large I was always satisfied that the painter had carried out sufficient work to justify the amount I was authorising. The crunch came at the final certificate stage by which time the 'extras' totalled several thousand pounds.

Before a final Subcontractor's certificate was sent through for payment it was usually sent to the Subcontractor to sign, signifying his acceptance of the amount as a final payment. I duly sent a certificate to the painter but omitted the several thousand pounds worth of extras. The next morning he was on the 'phone to tell me I had forgotten the extra monies. Five minutes later Ned F. was on the 'phone. 'I understand you won't certify the extra monies I've told you to pay the painter.'

'That's right.'

'Why not?'

'Because I don't know what they're for. It's nothing to do with my job.'

'But I've told you, two of the Directors have had their houses painted.'

'That's nothing to do with me.'

'But I've told you it's OK.'

'It's nothing to do with me. I won't certify it. I'll write out the certificate if you like but I won't sign it.'

And that's what happened. I sent an unsigned certificate to Ned F. I never found out what he did with it. For all I know he may have forged my signature on it.

*

Ned F. was a bit of a womaniser. I believe he had several regular girlfriends. At almost any club or restaurant I went into with him he was greeted by the receptionist like a long lost love 'Hello Ned darling, how are you?'

More than once at a Firm's annual dinner he buttonholed me.

'I'm going to disappear for half an hour or so. Entertain the old bag will you?'

'Eh?'

'Dance with my wife – chat her up.'

'Oh!'

Ned F. was about sixty years old when he collapsed and died from a heart attack. I was told several people received a telephone call from his wife enquiring if they might have any idea where he could have deposited his money. Apparently there was only £16 in his bank account!

*

Not everyone was dishonest.

One morning my brickie subbie came to see me.

'Here, guess what?'

'What?'

'Cecil Eves sent me a cheque for £2,000 yesterday.'

'What for?'

'Well I'm building the brickwork on his new bungalow.'

'So?'

'Well I didn't think he was going to pay me for it.'

'You weren't doing it for nothing were you?'

'No, but I thought I would be paid on one of the jobs.'

'There you go then, life's full of surprises!'

9

The Eleventh Commandment

One of the problems with fiddling – for the fiddler – is to avoid getting caught. The Eleventh Commandment: 'Thou shall not be found out'.

Some fiddlers go to elaborate lengths to avoid discovery only to slip up on something quite rudimentary. Tom was one such example. He was an intelligent fellow. He had, he said, been in the navy during the 1939–45 war and had risen to the rank of Lieutenant Commander. His story was that he had had three destroyers torpedoed beneath him. Whether or not all that was true, he had certainly developed a taste for gin from somewhere. All his money went on it, to the extent that he was always short of cash. I had been warned not to lend him any cash (a fine chance, I wasn't exactly overflowing with readies myself!).

Tom's dress was generally somewhat dishevelled and not-withstanding his intellect, he could not hold down a decent job. When I knew him he was a timekeeper/wages clerk on a large site. With hindsight that must have dangled temptation before him and, since his propensity for trying to borrow money was well known, it now seems surprising that he was even offered the job. He must have been supervised quite carefully; I don't think he was ever left alone with any cash. Nevertheless, it is a tribute to his consummate skill as a fiddler that he had quite a long run before he was caught almost by accident and by his own stupidity.

There were 80–100 men on the site. It was Tom's job to record the times they worked, which varied up to 50 or 60 hours per week. He simply recorded an hour or two extra for quite a few of them. He probably also turned a blind eye if any of them stopped off elsewhere during the day. Each week, after the wages payout, he would receive his kickback of approximately half the various overpayments. He was on to a good thing.

However, he had to do a quite enormous amount of book-keeping on his own account in order that he had a record of what he had paid to whom, and who owed him 50 per cent of it. Clearly he thought it was worth the effort and he got away with it successfully for about nine months. I suppose it increased the site wage bill by about 1 per cent – a small margin and difficult to pin down.

How was he caught? He went on holiday for two weeks and failed to make any transitional arrangements for the period of his absence. On the Thursday afternoon of the first week, his temporary replacement was astonished to find that when the wages were paid out in respect of the previous week when Tom had still been around, a stream of men came up to him and gave him various amounts of money. The temporary replacement was honest and Tom duly returned from his holiday to the sack and prosecution. Not however, before the site Office Manager had endured a number of sleepness nights in case it was thought that he had had a part in the fraud or that he should have detected it sooner.

10

Cover me Charlie

On one occasion I was detailed to carry out an investigation in connection with a contract in the north-east of England. I was to enquire into why a job, which had been making a healthy profit, had gone downhill in its last few months and had ended up making a very unhealthy loss.

There can be a number of reasons for this type of situation. The prices for the later trades or sections of the job might have been underestimated. Alternatively, as often happens, lots of 'bits and pieces' – 'odds and sods' in building parlance – may have been left unfinished in the earlier stages. It is very tempting for the site management to push on with the bulk items to achieve what appears to be rapid progress in those earlier stages, but the unfinished odds and sods can be left as a time bomb ticking away waiting to explode later.

The effect is two-fold. Not only do the unfinished items take a vastly disproportionate time to complete, they may also cost a vastly disproportionate amount. Moreover, the Contractor's Surveyor, when compiling his early valuations, may have completely ignored what then appeared to be only minor unfinished bits and pieces and thus have no money left in the kitty.

When I used to prepare valuations I was criticised on numerous occasions for being overly pessimistic because the job appeared to be making less profit than the 'powers-that-be' expected. 'Why is this bloody job in the red?' I would be asked.

'In the red' I came to realise over the years was merely a piece of Contract Manager's licence. When he said 'in the red' he did not mean the job was losing money. Quite probably he did not even mean that it was not making its estimated profit. What he really meant was that the job was not making what he thought it should be making but for my getting the valuation all wrong.

Nevertheless, unless I found an error in my figures somewhere – which might have happened from time to time – I stuck to my guns and insisted that my valuation reasonably represented the value of work which had been done.

The situation might have been something like this, taking as an example the excavation to a car-parking area attached to an office building. The bulk of the excavation would have been carried out early in the job leaving a small amount to be completed when the actual car park was constructed, or immediately prior to the landscaping near the end of the job.

Suppose that the total quantity of excavation was 10,000 cubic metres and that the Contractor's rate was £1.95 per cubic metre. That rate would have been built up by the estimator as an amalgam of machine and hand excavation – say 95 per cent by machine and 5 per cent by hand:

Machine:	9,500 cu m	@	£1.00	=	£9,500
Hand:	500 cu m	@	£20.00	=	£10,000
				Total	£19,500

÷ 10,000 cu m = average rate £1.95 per cubic metre

At the point early in the job when 9,500 cubic metres of excavation had been dug the 'true' value of the work was £9,500. That is the value the Surveyor should have calculated in his 'internal' valuation. However, since the contract rate was £1.95 per cubic metre there was really no reason why 9,500 × £1.95 totalling £18,525, should not have been included in the 'external' valuation. If £18,525 was included in the internal valuation the excavation work would have shown a large profit, but when the last 500 cubic metres came to be dug there would be a horrendous loss to be absorbed.

This example is slightly exaggerated because of the large difference in the value of machine and hand excavation. Nevertheless, a similar situation would prevail where comparatively small quantities of brickwork, concrete or plaster-work, for example, were left outstanding.

But to come back to my investigation in the north-east of England. I thought of the various possible reasons for the sudden deterioration in the financial fortunes of the job. The possibility of front-loading occurred to me. I spoke to the Chief Surveyor: 'Are the rates in the Bill of Quantities front-loaded?'

'What?'

'Are your Bill rates front-loaded?'

'There isn't a Bill.'

'What then?'

'A schedule of rates provided by the Client.'

'You mean the Client told us what rates to work for?'

'No. The schedule is divided into twelve sections. We do the work for various percentages on or off each section.'

'Well, who worked out the percentages?'

'The estimating department in London.'

'Have you got their calculations?'

'You're joking! They won't part with them. I've never seen an estimator's build-up.'

He was right. I remembered when I first joined the Firm I asked for the estimator's price build-up and was told exactly the same thing – 'they won't part with them'. However to the astonishment of everyone in the region where I was working at that time I managed to twist the estimator's arm and get a copy.

I did the same again for my inquest on the job in the north-east of England. Sure enough I found that for the sections of the work to be carried out in the early stages of the contract the estimator, having calculated that a tender of −10 per cent on the schedule

47

rates was required, actually quoted +10 per cent. For work in the latter stages he did the reverse, effectively heavily front-loading the tender. (See page 115).

All very laudable, if unethical in its own way, but he did not tell anyone and no one bothered to ask. They all rested on their laurels and had an easy time on the basis of the fat profit the job was making until it was too late.

The joke was that the Client – a very financially secure organisation – almost certainly realised what was going on. There were a number of design changes early in the job. If they had caused the Contractor to lose money he might well have been able to justify a claim for reimbursement. However, with the job turning in a handsome profit, a situation divined by the Client, that was always going to be difficult to say the least. Just who was conning whom?

*

I was fairly unimpressed by that department of the Firm in the North-East. When I arrived there the Manager greeted me. 'We've got you some great digs.'

'Digs? I'm not staying in digs. I'm staying in a hotel.'

'We can't afford that.'

'I'll go back home then. I'm not staying in digs. Head Office said I would be booked into a good hotel.'

I was duly booked into a hotel albeit it only a modest two star.

When I went on to the site, the site offices were absolutely filthy. There was a thick layer of dust over everything in every office except the Site Manager's; his had actually been decorated. Again, I threatened to leave in order to obtain a room and a desk that was usable. I also had to insist on being allowed to use the Manager's toilet.

I could not understand how anyone was prepared to work in such conditions and I said as much in the report I later produced. Out on the site a line of nine or ten toilets had been erected for the operatives to use. They were universally filthy and none of the cubicles were fitted with doors. I tackled the site Manager about this. 'I'm not having any of the buggers sitting there reading the paper!' was his answer.

I received some mild criticism over my report, not for the findings, which were fully accepted, but because I had – as it was put to me – failed to cover up some of the ancillary shortcomings, such as the filthy site offices. I really saw no reason to cover up anything. The whole attitude of the management was wrong in my opinion.

*

On another occasion, and in another part of the country, I did feel somewhat different. Again I had been detailed to ascertain why a job, which was originally doing well financially, had ended the day showing a loss.

I was in the area for about two weeks and ultimately came to the conclusion that the reason for the loss was interference by the departmental Manager. Towards the end of the job, for example,

he had insisted on the project being overloaded with labour and plant in an effort to ensure that it was completed on time. It should have been evident that even if this objective was attained the costings would be thrown to the winds.

All the staff had done well. The Chief Surveyor and the departmental Manager were both nice fellows. I was accommodated in a five-star hotel and moreover was wined and dined almost every evening – not that I allowed this to colour my judgement or my report!

My report stated all the factual conclusions I had come to and the reasons. I have to admit it might have been a bit difficult to discern them from the welter of information I provided. The report was addressed to the Commercial Manager at Head Office.

'I am not quite sure that I can see what you are driving at,' he said to me. 'I can see the reasons you point to for the loss, but nobody seems to be responsible.'

'Well, I suppose when you boil it down it's just one of those things. I can see how it happened. It was a bad job; we, get 'em now and again.'

In reality you could say I did a cover-up, but not just for the sake of it. I felt that all the staff had worked hard and done their best. It would have been grossly unfair for anyone to have been fired. Even the departmental Manager, who was probably the main culprit, was very capable in my opinion. In fact a few months later he was promoted to a very senior position in the Company at which I understand he was a great success. A tribute to my report!

*

The word 'cover' has a particular meaning in the context of construction tenders. It sometimes happens that when a contractor is invited to tender for a project, either he does not want to tender or, having agreed to do so, he finds himself unable to prepare his bid in the allotted time. In these circumstances, not wishing to reject the invitation to tender he may 'take a cover'. That is, he will contact another Firm that is preparing a tender and arrange to be informed about what price to submit, and perhaps even enter the prices in his copies of the Bills of Quantities. Of course, the price he is told to submit is higher than the Firm's own price by a modest margin.

On occasion more than one Firm decides to take a cover. Perhaps one Firm gives a cover to more than one other Firm. Or perhaps the Firm taking the cover is asked to provide a cover price by yet another Firm. Stories are rife where amongst half-a-dozen Firms tendering only one has prepared a bona-fide tender. In one instance I knew about, the cover price submitted was only marginally higher than the lowest tender submitted by the Firm that had provided it. Because the lowest tender is not always the one accepted there was considerable panic that the cover price might be accepted.

*

When I first arrived at the Firm's office in the North-East, having driven up from the South of England the Departmental Chief Surveyor welcomed me. I noticed him eyeing my car.

Many of the staff at that time were issued with Company cars. Apart from their job titles, the cars they drove were status symbols. For example, Surveyors were issued with smallish cars such as Ford Anglias or Vauxhall Vivas. Senior Surveyors drove larger cars such as Zephyr 4's, as indeed did Departmental Chief Surveyors for the first couple of years after their promotion. Then with luck they got the six-cylinder version, as did Contracts Managers.

I preferred to drive my own car and receive a car allowance rather than have a Company car. This meant I could choose it myself and more particularly, and prophetically as it turned out, I reasoned that if ever I were fired I would drive out of the gates. Nevertheless diplomacy required that if you chose your own car you selected one at about the right status level. My job title at that time was Senior Quantity Surveyor and a Jaguar, for example, might have been frowned upon.

However, I was driving over 30,000 miles per annum and for the small extra outlay involved I considered it was worth buying a Zephyr 6. The Firm ran quite a good scheme for those wishing to drive their own cars. They would lend the purchase price interest-free to be repaid over two years, in return for which the car was registered in the F irm's name for a year, in order to obtain a year's capital depreciation on it for tax purposes. It was all perfectly legal and above board and everyone was happy. Thus when I arrived in the North-East I was driving a car technically owned by the Firm although it was not a Firm's car in the normally accepted sense.

The Departmental Chief Surveyor eyed my Zephyr 6. 'Is that a Firm's car?' he asked.

'Yes,' I said casually.

I guessed what was going through his mind. I knew he was still driving a Zephyr 4.

'How did you get that then?'

'What do you mean?'

'The six-cylinder job.'

'Oh, I shrugged, 'I suppose they must think highly of me!'

11

A Hot Flush

I once came across a team of male bridge players who called themselves 'The Hot Flush'. They considered themselves 'hot stuff' at the game and the connotation of the word 'flush' with card games made the name seem apt. However, they were somewhat taken aback when they met the reaction of opposing ladies' teams who apparently thought the name either hilarious or disgusting. The men were overcome with embarrassment when someone explained to them why.

*

Spanish plumbing has something of a notorious reputation. Some years ago when on holiday in Spain there was a problem with the water supplies to the bedrooms in our hotel. For two or three hours we were asked not to use the baths or toilets. In due course the supplies were resumed and with some degree of relief I used the toilet. When I flushed it there were clouds of steam! Somewhere in the system the hot and cold supplies had been reversed. Quite a few people had hot flushes that day.

12

Semper in Excretum

Using the toilet as a child I remember wondering what actually happened when you pulled the chain. Where did it all go to? Working in the Construction Industry you soon find out!

There are basically two types of drainage system, surface water and foul. The former, as its name probably implies, deals with storm rainwater; the latter, with all other types of effluent, principally sewage. In some areas there are combined systems into which all wastes, including rainwater, are drained.

On the other hand, some areas have only foul drains, surface rainwater being discharged into soakaways comprising pits partially filled with stones to catch any silt or leaves etc., after which the liquid flows into the open ground. Remote areas have no main drainage at all. In those cases the sewage is collected in large containers, which rejoice in the name of septic tanks or cesspools. I have always felt they would be more appropriately called antiseptic tanks since they prevent the pollution of the surrounding ground. The tanks or cesspools have to be pumped out periodically and it is advisable to avoid overlooking when that operation is done!

The drainage pipes from a large building or a group of smaller buildings, such as houses, are connected to larger pipes, generally located under roads and referred to as sewers. Except in rare instances of sewers collapsing, sewers do not get blocked. Conversely the smaller foul drains serving buildings can easily become blocked by various household items. When a blockage occurs the pipe will gradually fill upstream of the obstruction slowly filling any intervening manholes. Sooner or later the blockage will become apparent by sewage becoming visible on garden lawns, or by toilets and sinks that will not empty. At that point some unfortunate soul is detailed to clear the blockage.

Some Firms exist solely to specialise in providing an emergency service to cater for such situations. Justifiably they charge a substantial amount for their expertise. But very often, for example on a new housing estate, Joe Bloggs or Paddy O'Reilly are commissioned to get the inhabitants out of trouble.

The first thing to do is to locate the actual source of the blockage. Lifting the cover of the nearest manhole will establish if the blockage is upstream of the manhole or not. This has to be done with some care because, if the blockage is downstream of the manhole, the chamber may well be full of excrement retained only by the sealed cover.

By carefully lifting the various manhole covers downstream, eventually one manhole will be found empty, disclosing that the source of the blockage is upstream of it. The cardinal rule when clearing a blocked drain is, wherever possible, to rod it from a position upstream of the blockage. This will ensure that when the blockage is released you are not in the path of the ensuing tidal wave. However, when the manholes upstream of the blockage are flooded it may well be quite impractical to rod the drain from these locations.

I remember one job located in an RAF station where the drains servicing the female barrack blocks were repeatedly blocked. There was a popular theory as to why. Be that as it may, the manholes were some 5 to 6 feet deep and the blockage on one occasion had to be cleared from a downsteam location because the manholes upstream of the blockage were all full. Joe – or Paddy – lowered himself into the first clear manhole downstream of the blockage and started rodding. He pushed and pushed and pushed, initially without success, until suddenly the blockage moved. Under the pressure of 6 feet head or so, the inlet to the manhole exploded around him. He scrambled to get out of the manhole but not before he was splattered from head to toe with the contents of the pipe.

Did he get any sympathy? Not a bit of it. Everyone around collapsed with laughter. At least he saw the funny side himself although the air was blue!

*

One large building had been handed over and occupied for some weeks. The weather, having been unusually dry, turned sour and one day there was a heavy thunderstorm accompanied by a torrential downpour. All the roads and car parks around the building flooded. Apparently no water was being drained away through the surface-water system. All the manholes were found to be full of water after the roads were partially cleared by pumping the flood-water away on to public roads.

The blockage appeared to be between the lowest manhole and the public sewer under the main road. The pumping continued until most of the water in the manholes and drains around the building had been removed.

Once again Joe or Paddy were detailed to start rodding and the rods were inserted into the exit pipe from the lowest manhole, that is the one nearest to the public sewer. Once again he pushed and pushed and pushed. The blockage, he announced, was only a few feet from the manhole, but try as he may he could not shift it.

There was nothing for it but to excavate the road surface on the downstream side of the manhole, dig down to expose the pipe and break it out to remove the obstruction. But there was nothing to break out! Apart from one length of pipe projecting from the side of the manhole there was no drain there. The entire surface-water drainage system serving the building, its roads and car parks had been laid complete but left unconnected to the sewer. Quite simply there was nowhere for the water to go.

How could this have happened? The answer was lack of

communication. The mistake had arisen due to a change of groundworks Foreman. The incoming Foreman had assumed, when he saw the lower sections of the drainage had been completed, that the connection to the sewer was in. Indeed, it was quite reasonable for him to have believed that since it is quite usual to commence drainage at the lowest end and work upwards. However, the connection to the sewer is sometimes left until later. On this occasion the outgoing Foreman had omitted to mention the fact. This did not prevent a lot of red faces and more blue air.

13

Many a Slip

Surplus materials left over when a job is completed can cause considerable embarrassment to the site management. It is virtually impossible to order exactly the right quantity of most materials. There is always some quite legitimate wastage and nobody can foresee exactly how much this will be.

Standard materials such as common bricks – that is those not generally visible in the completed building – are usually ordered in bulk at the start of a job and simply called up from the Supplier as and when required. However, many items are usually made for the job and once ordered have to be accepted and paid for. Even standard items, if returned to the Supplier, might only be credited at a part of their full value even if undamaged. Construction sites being what they are, this is a remote possibility.

Nevertheless, I suspect many Suppliers 'play the system', secure in the knowledge that they really can't lose. They will 'sting' the Contractor if he returns surplus materials; and if he finds he has under-ordered or 'lost' some of the items that have been delivered, they will sting him even more for supplying the small amounts or replacements that he will then require urgently.

'Urgently' might be the understatement of the year. In the closing stages of a job, missing vital items required to complete could result in the whole job not being handed over on schedule with all the resultant enormous costs and penalties that that implies.

Thus the prudent Contractor will ensure that he does not under-order any items if at all possible. The evil of over-ordering is small by comparison. So over-ordering often happens sometimes by accident, sometimes by design.

Just as common bricks can be ordered in bulk and called up when required, so can many of the more common facing bricks. However, there are hundreds of different types of facings, many of which are only manufactured when ordered. Since the lead time required between ordering and delivery might be three months, most Contractors will over-order such items.

It frequently happens, due to the design of a building, that facing bricks of special, non-standard sizes are required. In most cases these bricks are a standard size in outward appearance but perhaps only a third or half the standard thickness. They are referred to as 'slip' bricks and are often glued to the structural frame of the building with strong adhesive. If they are 'faced' on all sides they resemble the 'briquettes' often used for building brick fire surrounds. Thus I invariably found that such slip bricks were over-ordered! Which was an expensive luxury when you realise that, notwithstanding their smaller size, they usually cost about three or four times the price of the full-sized bricks. The quantities of slip bricks required on a job are generally comparatively small. If 100,000 full-sized bricks are needed the quantity of slips would probably be less than 500.

Such were the proportions required on a job in Central London where the Contractor entrusted the calculation of his requirements to the site Engineer. Whilst quite competent in engineering matters, he was somewhat out of his depth when it came to pure building items: he got a nought in the wrong and, as a result, 5,000 slips were ordered instead of 500.

Nobody realised anything was wrong until the brickwork on the job was well over fifty per cent complete and we still had nearly 5,000 slips on site. The problem then was what to do with them. The Supplier didn't want to know. A few were disposed of to build fireplaces but at the end of the day there were some 3,500 surplus to requirements.

There was only one thing to do: they were buried. The floor to the main entrance hall of the building had not yet been constructed and it required a moderate quantity of broken brick hardcore under it. And that was what it had – a moderate quantity of what was probably the most expensive hardcore in London.

*

Yet another example of a main entrance being involved in a cock-up was the case of the pink-tinted mirrors; the very expensive-pink tinted mirrors. The walls of part of this particular main entrance hall were lined with them. However, when they were fixed they were clearly unacceptable. All the reflections were distorted and the entrance hall was reminiscent of a fairground hall of mirrors. The Project Manager telephoned the Suppliers and demanded that the mirrors were replaced immediately. The Supplier agreed and said he had no use for the defective plates.

Two weeks later the replacements arrived and were duly fixed. The Project Manager went up the wall! The replacements were no better than the originals. This time the Supplier refused to deliver any more without making an inspection himself. Faces were rather more pink than the mirrors when he did! He took one look, got out his screwdriver and slackened off some of the fixing screws, many of which had been over-tightened thus causing the distortion.

Needless to say the Supplier now wanted paying for both consignments of the mirrors. And of course there were now a number of expensive pink-tinted mirrors surplus to requirements. There was no shortage of takers; the Architect had some, so did several of the Contractor's senior staff. To my chagrin I was working away from home at the time and had no means of delivering any to my own house.

14

Who's on the Take?

When I arrived at one power station job, construction was well advanced. I was new to the Firm and was posted there to assist the Quantity Surveyors who were somewhat behind hand with their measurements. So behind hand in fact that various sections of the work were actually completed. The measuring, concluded in due course, had been left unfinished either because of its complexity or because of the complete lack of site records as to what had actually been done, or both. What better job to give the new member of the organisation?

In due course I measured all the underground drainage, the routes of which appeared to have been decided on a day-to-day basis for there was no comprehensive layout plan. I measured all the underground tunnels and shafts, and all the services in them. I also measured what are called the turbo-blocks. These are essentially giant blocks of reinforced concrete on which the turbo-generators that produce the electricity are mounted. As I recollect, these blocks were some 100 feet long, 30 or 40 feet wide and about 50 or 60 feet high. They were riddled with crevices, niches, ducts and channels etc. to accommodate the many pipes, cables and the cooling water that was extracted from the nearby river and returned at a higher temperature. So complicated were the turbo-blocks to construct that mere working drawings were insufficient. Sectional hardwood models were also provided, which thankfully I had the use of when doing the measuring.

There were also some large underground tanks which had been constructed in reinforced concrete. These were also quite complicated but the drawings were reasonably concise. What was not clear from the drawings was the detailing of the mastic asphalt tanking, which had been applied to the outside of the tanks to waterproof them. I had to measure that too, although by that time it was completely concealed by beautifully turfed lawns.

Initially I thought that would not be a great problem as I had to agree the measurements with the specialist Subcontractor who had laid the tanking. Although I would have to rely on his honesty to some extent, at least he would know what was there – or so I thought. But no such luck. The chap who appeared at the meeting to agree the measurements had not seen the job done, had no idea what was there and, what was more, his supervisor who did know had left him and there was no one else available. The two of us sat down to measure the work, a classic case of the blind leading the blind. At least the saving grace was that there was no one around who could argue with our figures.

*

Before I arrived on that job a brazen piece of highway robbery had been attempted.The turbo-generators were to be electrically earthed by a network of heavy copper strips embedded in the floor finish to the generator house. The strips had been laid prior to the completion of the floor finish when a small gang of men in white overalls began lifting them. They proceeded to coil them up and load them into a van. Incredibly no one challenged them or, if they did, they received a convincing explanation.

The coils duly loaded, the gang drove out of the generator house and on to the exit road leading to the main gates. There the van broke down and the men were apprehended by a keen-eyed gatekeeper who smelt a rat when he saw what was inside.

*

Occasionally things are literally 'borrowed' rather than stolen.

Not quite like the embezzler who borrows some funds genuinely intending to return them after his horse has won; sometimes the items really have been borrowed.

I remember a site Supervisor who was constantly 'phoning me on one pretext or another, trying to persuade me to remove Subcontractors from his job. I do not remember any instance where I was satisfied that there were sufficient grounds to remove them. With hindsight I suspect he wanted them removed because they would not agree to carry out some work on his house. But at the time, in my naive innocence, that thought did not occur to me. However some Subcontractors, I later found out, were not so scrupulous and regularly did him favours for which, no doubt, the Firm ultimately paid.

It was therefore with some satisfaction that I heard of a debacle concerning him. I presume he must have been unable to obtain the services of a Subcontractor at the time. Alternatively, he saw what appeared to be an even simpler method of achieving what he wanted, which was apparently to move some earth around in his front garden prior to constructing a wall.

A local builder who was working nearby had left his JCB excavator parked next to the roadway about 100 yards from the Supervisor's house. The Supervisor decided to borrow it and succeeded in starting the engine, but the machine proved more difficult to drive than he had anticipated. He collided with a car and then ran into a garden wall. Considerable damage was done to the JCB, the car and the wall although fortunately no one was hurt. The book, as they say, was thrown at him. Taking away a vehicle whilst unlicensed; ditto whilst uninsured; driving without due care, thus causing damage to property.

15

Disappearing Act

Last night upon the stair,
I met a man who wasn't there.
He wasn't there again today,
Oh how I wish he'd go away.

(Origin unknown)

Nowadays the Inland Revenue have tightened up on Sub-contractors in the Construction Industry to try and ensure that they all pay their income tax. Subcontractors who are up to date with their tax affairs are issued with Tax Exemption Certificates, enabling Main Contractors to pay them without deducting tax. This is particularly important for 'labour-only' Subcontractors who are employed purely to supply labour to fix or install materials bought and paid for by the Main Contractor. Any Subcontractor without a Tax Exemption Certificate has income tax deducted at the standard rate. Believe it or not, there are quite a few subbies who are content to work on this basis rather than fill in a tax return and get pulled into the net for previous tax arrears.

Before this system was inaugurated – and at that time there was still virtually full employment – many operatives found it better to work on a self-employed basis rather than as straightforward Employees. It was particularly advantageous to do this because, until they completed a tax return and were thus known to the tax man, they paid no income tax. Because of the shortage of labour many Main Contractors found they could only obtain good operatives in this way. The output of the best operatives was much higher than the general average; indeed it was not unknown for a top-class operative to produce two or three times the average and without any loss of quality.

From time to time my Subcontractor Clients would ask me to measure the work they had done each week or check their Foreman's figures to verify that their men had produced sufficient to justify their earnings. Many of the operatives were paid on a piece-work basis and the outputs of some were quite astonishing.

On one job where my Client was the bricklayer Subcontractor the Main Contractor had said he expected eight to ten bricklayers on the project. Bricklayers at that time were very scarce indeed. My Client provided two bricklayers and one labourer (the usual skilled/unskilled proportion is 2:1) Incredibly the Main Contractor's programme was achieved with just the two craftsmen.

On another job my Client was the Formwork Subcontractor. He supplied labour and material to construct the temporary falsework and moulds into which the Main Contractor poured liquid concrete. As it happened the Main Contractor had started the job using his own labour to construct the formwork. He had forty carpenters on the job but he found that not only was the work costing him too much, but he was getting behind programme. He engaged my Client to take over and on a rule-of-thumb basis that the Main Contractor had had forty men on the site, my Client put on twenty.

Progress was good but I had to tell my Client that he was losing money and that he needed to reduce his labour force to fourteen or fifteen men and maintain the same output. Not to be outdone he cut his labour strength to 12, worked weekends and stayed on the site himself full-time. Output actually increased and my Client eventually made a good profit.

The Main Contractor employed a work-study engineer to record outputs and progress. He commented to me one day that he was quite amazed at the progress being being achieved by my Client with only twenty-two men!

Before the Inland Revenue tightened up on the system, the only information self-employed men provided to Main Contractors, or the Subcontractors they worked for, was their name. As a general rule the information they gave was accepted at its face value. The system was referred to colloquially as 'The Lump'. On occasions men would work for a few weeks under one name, disappear for a while and reappear under a different name. There were many Smiths, Joneses, Murphys and O'Briens etc. I heard of one case – probably mythical – where one man worked his way through the names of a well-known football team. The story probably was apocryphal because I heard a similar tale regarding the names one Contractor utilised to make a spurious claim for wage inflation costs.

One Client – a 'labour-only' carpentry and joinery Sub-contractor – asked me to verify his Foreman's wage-earning figures for his men. His carpenters mostly worked in pairs. This was a while ago when most chippies earned £60–£70 per week. Generally they aspired to 'make the ton' that is to earn £100, as bricklayers mostly did at that time.

One pair of chippies – their names were Wilson and Dimambo – usually earned about £220 between them. I only ever saw Wilson and, because of the name, imagined Dimambo to be a chap of African origin. After some time I thought it odd that not only had I not seen Dimambo but that I had not seen any African chippy at all. I asked around and finally bottomed it, as they say. Dimambo did not exist. He was a phantom. Wilson was a loner who worked all hours. He apparently submitted his tax return to the Inland Revenue and duly paid 'his' tax – but not Dimambo's!

16

Who's a Naughty Boy/Girl?

It is not unusual, even on large projects or perhaps especially on large projects, for one of the Directors of the constructing Firm to appear at a site meeting at short notice or even without notice. This ostensibly gives him an insight into the job and shows everyone concerned that he is taking an interest. If he is sensible he will merely sit and listen to the discussion; if he is not, he might weigh in in support of his staff with only a partial understanding of what the discussion is about. Either way, his presence will probably inhibit the proceedings to the extent that a supplementary meeting will be necessary after he has left the site, at which all the problems, including the various cock-ups, can be aired freely.

Many years ago, whilst still a junior surveyor, I was sometimes allowed to sit in on site meetings. This was considered good experience for me and also meant that I was immediately available to organise the tea or run any errands. The project was a large one, as was the contracting organisation. The Project Surveyor – my immediate superior – attended all the site meetings as, of course did the Site Agent and Engineer.

On one occasion, one of the Directors turned up for a site meeting accompanied by his rather attractive married secretary. We had had advance warning of his arrival by a somewhat devious route as the Project Surveyor was in the throes of an illicit affair with the secretary. He had casually mentioned that 'he had heard' that the Director intended to visit the site for the meeting. His affair had been strongly rumoured for some time. I had been instrumental in fleshing out the rumours by dint of the fact that I was often detailed to man the telephone switchboard when the Site Agent took the telephone operator to lunch. It was frequently during lunch hours that the Project Surveyor telephoned his paramour at head office! 'Was nothing sacred?'

The site meeting duly took place and afterwards the Director decided on a tour of the site that comprised amongst other things, a large reinforced concrete structure, access to the top of which was via a 50 foot vertical iron cat ladder. Climbing vertical ladders can be quite nerve wracking to the uninitiated, but the Director was quite insistent. To everyone's surprise his secretary was equally insistent that she wanted to accompany him. She clearly had no fear of heights and had no worries about the fact that she was wearing a skirt.

The Director started to ascend the ladder. The Project Surveyor made a point of guiding the secretary to the foot of the ladder so that she could follow behind her Boss. My superior was heard to tell her to hold on tight and not to worry because he was right behind her. This caused considerable amusement to those of us watching because he wasn't so much right behind her as right underneath her. Bets were quickly taken.

'I bet you five bob he looks up.'

'No he won't.'

'Five bob then?'

'Done!'

Money thrown away. He wasn't even halfway up the ladder before he looked up. 'Just to make sure she was OK,' as he later explained!

Some years later in a senior position I had to attend the site meetings of several jobs. On one site the Architect – that is the individual who dealt with the day-to-day architectural running of the job – was a lady of about thirty years of age. She was an attractive 5'2" or 5'3" tall. It was the era of the mini-skirt and she used to visit sites clad in one of mid-thigh length. She certainly looked very fetching, especially when she was wearing leather boots. When she went round the site, work virtually stopped particularly when she went up and down the ladders and on to the scaffolds. Her name was Julie.

About every alternate site meeting her immediate Boss used to accompany her. He was in his late forties or early fifties and he had a very severe manner of speaking. In fact whenever he spoke to Julie he seemed to reprimand her. 'Have you issued the details of those fittings?'

'Er, no not yet.'

'Oh, Julie! Why not?'

'They're not finished yet.'

'But they are urgent.'

'They'll be done this week.'

'See that they are!'

More than once I felt that at any moment he was going to give her a spanking. He never did, at least not on the site.

17

Give us a Break ...

Wherever there are windows there are going to be breakages; it is a fact of life. The more windows there are, the more breakages – or so you would think. But somehow it doesn't work out like that. Some jobs have hundreds of windows and yet only the occasional breakage. This will happen – Sod's Law again – where the type of glass or glazing is comparatively cheap. Get a job where expensive glass is specified or, for example, there are sealed double-glazing units, or both, no end of windows will be broken.

Sealed units are particularly expensive and when broken cannot generally be repaired on site. They have to be reordered from the factory, whereas the Glazier can visit the site and replace an ordinary pane of glass there and then. Not cheap, but bearable. Large panes of plate glass, such as those used for shop windows are of course very expensive to replace by virtue of their size, which also means that they have to be made of thicker glass.

Glaziers generally carry insurance on their work, or alternatively will price a 'breakage allowance' into all their tenders. However, they are only responsible for the glass until they have glazed it into the structure. On occasions – in a weak moment – they will agree to accept responsibility for the glass until the point at which the building is handed over to the Client; or they may find that, because of some obscure or ambiguous wording in their contract with the Main Contractor, they are liable in that way. Since they have no control over what happens after they have finished their work and left the site, any such passing of the buck to them by the Main Contractor is really an ingenious subterfuge or yet another 'Hey Diddle Diddle' on the Contractor's part.

Sometimes, however, the boot can be on the other foot. Because, short of some blatant negligence on the part of the Contractor, the Glazier is responsible for the glass until it is glazed, in no circumstances should the Contractor agree to handle the glass except at the Glazier's risk. Nevertheless, Contractors are sometimes talked into handling crates of glass officially or unofficially without that disclaimer. I suspect it is more often than not unofficial. As always, everything is all right until something goes wrong, but, when it does go wrong, it can be disastrous.

One job sticks in my mind from quite a few years ago; I must admit I still find it amusing to recollect. I was the Project Surveyor resident on the site. At first-floor level there was what can only be described as a gigantic patio. There were some ten or twelve very large glass windows with sliding door sections. The plates of glass were either ⅜″ or ½″ thick. In value they were then worth £500–£600 each; at today's values probably £3,000–£4,000 each. All told there were about 20 panes of glass.

The glass arrived in two large crates. We had a large mobile crane on the site and the Glazier arranged with the General Foreman that it would lift the crates up to the first floor 'as a favour'. It was in fact a very large favour and the General Foreman was probably going to do quite well out of it.

The actual lifting operation was quite tricky because at first-floor level there was a screen wall, some 3 metres high, around the patio. This meant that at ground level the crane driver could not see the patio on to which he was to lower the crates. It also meant that the crates had to be lifted high over the screen wall to obviate any danger of them touching it. Each crate was worth about £6,000; at today's values about £40,000.

At the top of a ladder leaning against the screen wall, perched the Banksman – the man who guided the crane driver by a series of conventional hand signals. The first crate containing ten plates of glass was lifted high over the screen wall and in response to the Banksman's hand signals, was lowered to within a few inches of the patio. The Glazier's men were then able to guide it down those last few inches.

What exactly caused what happened next was never clear, but the corner of the crate hit the patio floor rather hard. The panes of glass were well packed. If the crate had struck the floor evenly along one side it is probable that no damage would have ensued. As it was striking the corner of the crate was the Achilles heel; when the crate was opened every plate except one was cracked.

The recriminations started. The Foreman Glazier blamed the Banksman. The Banksman blamed the Crane Driver. The Crane Driver blamed the Banksman; as a second line of defence he said the crane's clutch had slipped.

Whatever the rights and wrongs the result was nine very broken, very large, very expensive plates of glass which were going to take two weeks to replace – once the replacements were ordered. The Glazier made it quite clear he had no intention of ordering them unless we, the Contractor, agreed to pay for them.

For our part we said the glass was the Glazier's responsibility before it was fixed and that, if it was insured, the Glazier's Insurers should foot the bill, otherwise it was the Glazier's own problem. It was insured and everyone breathed a sigh of relief until the Glazier's Insurers discovered that the crate of glass was being lifted by our crane. They immediately denied liability. However, they pointed out that the Contractor's insurance cover would include damage caused to materials on the site. Our insurers decidedly disagreed. The policy covered only the Contractor's materials; the glass belonged to the Glazier.

After two weeks of argument the deadlock was finally broken by one of those compromises that pleased no one. We accepted a third of the replacement cost, the Glazier accepted a third and the final third was very reluctantly shared by the two insurers.

However, the saga did not end there. After the replacements

arrived and all the plates of glass were fixed, it continued in circumstances strongly reminiscent of a pantomime farce.

A man carrying a steel scaffold tube on his shoulder was called by a mate. He turned, swinging the end of the tube around in the process, and duly shattered one of the panes. A few days later, another man with a scaffold board on his shoulder, had a lapse of concentration and, used to walking though the open sliding sections overlooked the fact that one was closed, and walked straight through it. My boss was on his 'phone to me: 'What the hell are you doing down there. I hear you've broken yet another plate-glass window.'

'Not me personally.'

'Well, you're part of the management team.'

'Am I?' It was news to me.

'Yes, you bloody well are and I'm fed up with hearing about broken plate-glass windows. So is the Insurance Company. They've refused to pay for the last breakage, so they sure as hell won't pay for this one.'

'Oh!'

So the job had to pay for the cost of replacements, but that still was not the end of the saga.

A week or two later the paving to the patio area was being laid. The materials were being moved around by a dumper, a machine fitted with an open compartment for carrying materials with a tipper mechanism. It can move equally well either forwards or backwards, and the driver has a swivel seat enabling him to face in either direction.

On this occasion the driver, feeling the need to respond to a call of nature, had left the machine just outside one of the glass windows and had gone off leaving the engine running. Exasperated at the machine being left in his way, one of the Paviors jumped into the driving seat, slammed the machine into gear and moved off. Unfortunately he slammed it into the wrong direction and drove straight through the window. Needless to say the insurers did not want to know about that one either!

18

It's an Ill Wind

One site in the Midlands was almost an encapsulation of the Building Industry as a whole. Not only was it an embodiment of Sod's Law but, to those of my disposition, it produced the type of situation where if you couldn't laugh you could only cry. It even had its share of tragedy.

The job was a housing site of medium size. The houses were being speculatively built and were of varying types. At the time I was responsible as the Contractor's Surveyor for the quantity surveying on a number of jobs. Some were housing jobs but a few were large building and civil engineering contracts. This particular site was centrally situated and it was thus very convenient for me to be based there and use it as my 'headquarters'.

The usual things went wrong on the site, for example, some windows were lost, and at least one house was built with its entrance door at the front when in fact it should have been at the side. But there were two other more serious cock-ups that caused an above-average degree of hassle.

The site was on sloping ground. This meant the houses were built at various levels, both in relation to each other and to the adjacent road. The Designers naturally endeavoured to avoid excessive excavation or filling to the foundations as far as possible by following the natural ground contours. However the junction of a new estate road with the existing road is preordained, as are the maximum gradients to which the new roads can be laid. Once the new road levels are determined, the levels of the houses can be worked out. They have to relate to the road, but within certain parameters they can vary up or down.

Adjoining semi-detached houses do not have to be built at the same level. They can be 'stepped' at their party walls. Similarly, where a house has an 'attached' garage, that is one joined to the house but not actually integral with it, the garage floor level is independent of the house floor level to some degree. If the garage is completely detached it is, of course, quite independent of the house level but the cost-saving of utilising a common wall between the two is lost. The level of the garage floor obviously has to relate to the road since the driveway gradient is limited. Consistent with that, the garage will normally be constructed at the original ground level to avoid any unnecessary excavation or filling under the floor.

One particular house was built on ground well below the road level. To avoid the garden pathways having to be too steep or have steps, the floor was made up and thus required some fill material beneath it. The attached garage was constructed at a lower level to save on 'make-up' material under both the garage and its drive-way. This resulted in the gradient of the driveway being steeper than the pathways, but this actually made for quite an attractive appearance landscape-wise.

Appearances apart, it also made putting a car into the garage quite a hazardous operation. The junctions at the top and bottom of the driveway had to be curved to prevent any part of the vehicle touching the ground. That was done when the driveway was laid but it was with some trepidation that the new owner drove his car into the garage for the first time. He drove it in, but then found that he had to wait for his engine to warm up before he could get it out. Obviously in icy weather it would have been impossible. After much heart-searching it was finally decided that the garage would have to be demolished and reconstructed at a higher level – as always at considerable cost.

The cost of that operation was dwarfed by the cost of overcoming the other calamity that befell:

A number of houses similarly built on ground below the road level also required a considerable amount of make-up fill material to raise them to acceptable levels. Needless to say, it is essential to well consolidate such material to avoid any problems of settlement at a later date. In the case of one house, that had not been done. No steel reinforcing mesh had been incorporated in the concrete floor slab to assist in avoiding settlement and, some weeks after the house was occupied, cracks began to appear in the floors.

The occupants reported the matter to the Contractor. After a couple of weeks it was quite evident that the cracks were getting worse and a rapid decision was made to avoid any adverse publicity. The occupants were moved into an expensive hotel for four weeks whilst the whole of the ground-floor slab was broken out and reconstructed. Their furniture and belongings were put into store and the entire ground floor of the house required redecoration. All in all a very expensive operation indeed!

*

On a nearby but very much larger housing site, the General Foreman caused great amusement by marking up the site plan on his office wall with symbols indicating which of the new houses were progressively occupied by what he euphemistically referred to as 'talent'. The site was quite extensive and he would frequently make his rounds on a bicycle. Equally frequently he would disappear for a couple of hours or so 'inspecting for any defects' in the occupied houses.

On the site where I was resident it was not the Foreman who provided the entertainment but one of the new occupants. One of the more expensive houses on the estate, situated opposite my site office, was occupied by a man serving in the RAF. He worked at a nearby RAF establishment and was apparently permitted to live outside. His wife was quite definitely rather attractive.

A few doors away, one of the new houses was occupied by a commercial traveller and his equally attractive spouse. Both of them and the RAF man used to depart for work at about 8.30 each morning. By ten o'clock the salesman was back, but not at his own house. Almost every day he used to visit the RAF man's wife. We theorised as to why, until one day they treated us to a grandstand performance. There they were in the ground-floor lounge, the curtains undrawn, the wife leaning over the settee ...

This story has a sad and rather tragic end. The RAF man – in his thirties – collapsed and died from a heart attack whilst at work one day. The more irreverent ones among us commented, referring to his wife, 'Well, she won't be hard up for someone to comfort her.'

We were not far wrong. Within a week the salesman had resumed his daily calls.

This brings me to the story – almost certainly apochryphal – of the driver of the liquid concrete wagon who suspected that his wife was having an affair. One day, driving past his house he saw a mini parked outside. A couple of hours later, with 7 cubic yards of concrete on board, he drove past again. The mini was still there. He promptly backed up and discharged his full load over the mini, completely burying it. 'That'll teach the bastard,' he thought. 'The bastard' turned out to be the plumber who the wife had called in to repair their central heating boiler.

*

From time to time I was visited by a professional Quantity Surveyor in connection with a civil engineering contract I was dealing with. He represented our Client, an oil company as it happens, although this has no particular relevance. He was highly amused by the antics of the commercial traveller, not to say disappointed that he had not been visiting me on the occasion of the public performance.

At lunch time we generally adjourned to a local country restaurant, after which we would return and resume our labours. His wife being a vegetarian, he invariably took the opportunity to have what he described as 'a bloody good blow out' when we went to lunch. This had its effect and at intervals during the afternoon he would say, 'I must just step outside,' where he would break wind in isolation and with great gusto. He was rather embarrassed and would occasionally ask, 'Did you hear that?'

'No,' I would say.

He never queried what it was I was supposed not to have heard, if I hadn't heard it. Anyway, at about mark ten on the Richter scale, I should think the whole estate heard it.

19

Where There's no Sense ...

Nowadays safety is taken very seriously on construction sites. That is to say, the Safety Regulations are very much stricter than they used to be. Nevertheless, they are frequently ignored and quite unnecessary risks are taken. For example, many sites are often littered with pieces of wood many of which have nails protruding from them point-up. I have to admit that I do not wear protective footwear with hard toe caps and metal sole inserts.

But for many years I have *never* set foot on a site without wearing a hard hat – I would not feel safe. And yet, even though the wearing of hard hats is now compulsory by law, operatives may still be seen without them. It is also quite commonplace to see operatives using grinding wheels without eye shields or breathing masks.

Some time ago I saw a labourer burning some polystyrene debris which gives off highly toxic fumes when set alight. He was standing on the downwind side of the flames and he was all but engulfed in smoke.

'You know that smoke is very poisonous!' I said to him.

'Is that a fact?' he said, and carried on as though I had not said anything.

When I think of the risks I used to take when I was young I shudder. I would walk on single scaffold boards 225 mm (9″) wide with a 50- or 60-foot drop on either side and think nothing of it. Or I would similarly walk along the top of steel beams of a partly erected steel framework.

Generally only the man erecting such frameworks – the spiderman – gets up to such antics. Spidermen are not too particular about kicking off nuts, bolts or even spanners as they walk on the beams. Some of the bolts may be 25 mm (1″) in diameter, the nuts 75 mm (3″) or more, with spanners to suit. I once had such a spanner land within a metre or so of me after it had fallen about 80 feet. It could have given me quite a headache even with a hard hat on my head. A nut falling from such a height might well perforate a hard hat and could kill anyone not wearing one.

And yet on one job I remember a piece of masonry falling from the fifth floor level and striking a man at ground level what must have been a glancing blow on the head. He was not wearing a hard hat and suffered a fractured skull, but he was back at work a few weeks later.

Whilst many accidents are tragic and can never be remotely funny, others do have a humourous aspect to them either in retrospect, or at least when it has become evident that the victim has not been seriously hurt. The man who slips on the banana skin is only funny provided he is unhurt.

I remember one job involving a staff restaurant being constructed in a basement. A brick ventilation duct had been built from the basement ceiling level right up to the roof, eight or nine floors higher. At the last moment it was decided that the interior of the brick duct – which was less than one metre square – should be plastered. The only way it could be done was to lower a man from the top in a bosun's chair. During intervals when he was not working in the duct, the chair was left suspended in it.

Somehow the ropes holding the chair became loose and it fell some sixty feet to the basement. Sod's Law again – there was a man underneath at the time and he was struck full on the head. He was not wearing a hard hat at the time and, although the bosun's chair may have 'floated' in the duct and thus have been slowed in its descent, the man was rendered unconscious and taken to hospital. He quickly recovered consciousness, was x-rayed, found to be all right and was back on site the same day. Being Irish the poor fellow got little sympathy. 'Where there's no sense there's no feeling,' everyone said.

*

On another job nearing completion the large basement area was being swept out. There was quite a lot of drainage running beneath it, with various access manholes. It is not uncommon for the cast-iron covers to such manholes to be set in position very late in the job. Prior to that the manholes are covered with boards, such as plywood sheets, to prevent anyone falling into them.

One of the men sweeping out the basement, seeing what he idly thought was a sheet of plywood in his way, picked it up to move it and stepped forward into the manhole it was covering. Fortunately what could have been a nasty fall resulted in only minor injuries and once again evoked more laughter than sympathy.

*

Rubbish is generally discharged from the upper levels of a building under construction by means of a chute. I have also seen lift shafts used for this purpose. On other occasions, I have seen the rubbish simply thrown off the scaffold or out of the building to form a heap beneath. Not only is this unsympathetic to the environment because of the dust it creates, but is also very dangerous.

On one job the navvy collecting the rubbish and debris on the upper floor doubtless considered he was taking proper precautions to safeguard those below. He may well have been right because he was making such a mess that no one in their right mind would have been anywhere near the pile of debris at ground level. Nevertheless, the only concession he made to safety as he threw each shovel of rubbish out of the fifth floor window was to shout, 'Below!'

*

Some victims of accidents have only their own carelessness to blame. Probably the most flagrant example of this, in my experience occurred some years ago.

Many sites utilise what are known as barrow or platform hoists. They are so called because the part that goes up and down comprises a flat platform, which can be stopped at each floor level. It is then possible to wheel a barrow onto the platform for raising or lowering to another level. Personnel are prohibited from riding on the platform, although once again in my younger days before safety regulations were so strict it was allowed and I have done it many times.

When the hoist is operated the platform can be lowered at high speed to be slowed and stopped with accuracy at each level. The guide and runners to the hoist mechanism, together with the platform, are generally enclosed by a scaffold framework with wire mesh and a sliding door at each access point. There may well be sliding doors on two sides to enable barrows or materials to be placed on to or removed from the hoist, both from the building and the scaffolding around it.

Such was the situation on one particular job when a member of staff wishing to gain access to the building opened the outer sliding door intending to walk through the hoist tower and into the building via the inner door. As he stepped into the tower the loaded platform descended at speed and poleaxed him. But for the fact that he was wearing a safety helmet he would undoubtedly have been killed, never knowing what hit him. As it was he was seriously injured, suffering a fractured skull amongst other things. He returned to work after some three months vowing to take legal action against the Firm. Wisely, in my opinion, he never did.

20

Cheer up! It May Never Happen

When you address a meeting the standard edict is that you should speak slowly and clearly. Similarly when you give someone an instruction it is advisable to do the same. It is very easy to overlook the fact that the person receiving the instruction may have far less knowledge of the matter in hand than you do. Consequently, what is obvious to you may be by no means obvious to them. Additionally, maybe the job you want them to do is one you feel they will be reluctant to accept. They will need a bit of 'chatting-up'; a bit of 'encouragement', in short a bit of bullshit.

I have experienced a variety of tactics over the years when my seniors have endeavoured to persuade me to do something, or perhaps to take up residence somewhere, that they anticipated I would be likely to argue against.

The first ploy is usually to heap a few compliments on you; what a good job you have been doing and so on. They will tell you they have considered a number of different people for the job and have come to the conclusion that you are undoubtedly the best and that only you will do. You feel wanted! At some point in the process of persuasion they will tell you that what they are proposing presents you with a *challenge* which you would not want to evade. (I used to have a little bet with myself on how long it would be before the word challenge was mentioned.)

The last thing they would mention was money. If I continued to show reluctance there would eventually be a hint that some financial improvement in my circumstances might be possible. If a relocation was involved the words 'financial improvement' had to be defined very carefully. If the proposed move was from the south of England to the North, I would be told how much cheaper it was to live in the North, and how much cheaper houses were to buy. There was some truth in this, but in an era when there was full employment in the South but not in the North, only an increase in salary would be likely to persuade anyone to move from south to north. The problem was that working in the South my salary was probably already higher than the person I would be working under up North.

If the move proposed was from North to South, a small increase in salary would probably be offered, coupled with the advice that whilst houses were more expensive in the South, I had to bear in mind the considerable increase in asset value I would obtain.

Sometimes it might be decided that a particular member of staff was expendable. The firm actually wanted him to leave. Offering him a transfer to an unpalatable part of the country – like Northern Ireland – might be one way of dropping him the hint. Changing his Company car would be another ploy; that is changing it for a pool car or an inferior model. On one occasion a chap who weighed twenty stone had his executive car changed for a Ford Anglia. After three months he took the hint and left.

Hints are all very well but sometimes they can be mis-intepreted, or perhaps not intended as hints at all. I often bemoan the fact that my natural facial expression is one of seriousness. People are always saying to me 'cheer up, don't look so worried'. I'm not really worried, I may just be deep in thought, but I envy those who can always look cheerful.

One Site Supervisor I worked with did not actually look cheerful but he did contrive – whether intentionally or otherwise – always to have a grin on his face. Unfortunately it was just a grin not a smile, and it gave him rather a cynical, quizzical look. As it happened his chief, the Contracts Manager, was a moderately

After three months he took the hint ...

cheerful fellow but he suffered from a twitch in one eyelid. This could have easily been mistaken as a wink, particularly as he was in the habit of winking anyway. If he gave an instruction to the Site Supervisor the poor fellow was never quite sure whether to take it literally or to assume that, because of the wink, he was actually intended to ignore the instruction or even to do the opposite. He would often sit smiling cynically to be rudely awakened by: 'What the hell are you sitting there grinning for?'

*

My chief at one time was very forthright; his instructions very concise. He used to arrive at the office at five to nine every morning. By nine o'clock his secretary had a standing instruction to bring him a pot of coffee. On the odd occasion that she didn't manage it by five past nine he would fling open the door to his office and bellow down the corridor in his Irish brogue: 'Where's me ****ing coffee?'

The canteen assistant on one site was Harold, who rather fancied himself as a waiter I think. He used to dress in what had been a smart black suit, white shirt and black tie. He called us all 'Sir'. The Project Manager generally ate only a snack lunch. One day, as ordered, Harold brought him a hamburger and a cup of tea. The Manager was on the telephone at the time and ten minutes later when he looked at his hamburger it was cold. 'Harold,' he shouted.

Harold scurried in. 'Yes, sir?'

'Heat that.'

'Yes sir.'

Ten minutes elapsed.

'Harold.'

'Yes, sir?'

'Where's my ****ing hamburger?'

'I've eaten it, sir.'

'What do you mean you've eaten it?'

'You told me to eat it, sir.'

'I did not.'

'Yes sir, you said to eat it.'

'I said to heat it not eat it.'

'Oh, sorry sir!'

*

Sometimes someone can say something to you that in isolation is complete gibberish, although they know what they mean and you know what they mean.

On one site a number of terraces of town houses – that is, three-storey houses – were being built. Each house had a balcony leading from the lounge at first-floor level. The balcony floors were finished with weatherproof tiles laid on plywood, which was in turn fixed to timber joists. In order to provide a fall or slight slope for drainage purposes, each joist had another piece of timber – a firring – fixed on top. The fall was obtained by the difference in the thickness of the firrings on each joist.

The drawings were not too clear as to the thickness of the firrings or how many there were to be. Standing on a balcony that had already been boarded out, I said to the Foreman chippy who, as it happens, was Irish and always had a cheerful glint in his eye. 'How many of these joists have got firrings?'

'Well, there's seven, only the end one hasn't got one!'

I knew just what he meant.

21

What the Left Hand Doesn't Know ...

Probably the most frequent of errors on building sites concern 'handing'. On the face of it, there should be no problem. There are generally only two possible answers – right or left hand – but perhaps Sod's Law rears its head again. If a drawing or working detail is vaguely ambiguous and the 'left hand' alternative is decided upon, it is almost preordained that it will be the 'right-hand' version that was required.

To appreciate the problem, consider first the instance where there should be no problem at all, namely a pair of semi-detached houses. Generally each one of the pair is the mirror image of the other. Thus all doors, windows, fittings etc. can be ordered in equal numbers of right and left hand. For example, if there are 20 pairs of a particular type of semi, then 20 left-hand and 20 right-hand sink tops will be required. If early on a right-hand one is fitted instead of a left hand, a little time bomb is set ticking, because when the plumber comes to fit the last right-hand one he finds that he only has a left-hand one in the store.

Not all semi-detached houses are mirror images. Sometimes the Architect decides it would make a change to have both houses in the pair built to the same hand – not on all of the pairs you understand, just on some of them. On those pairs the two houses will be – or should be – identical. Sometimes one house of a pair will be located on a corner, that is at the junction of a main road with a side turning. In that case, the 'front' entrance door may well be at the side of the house and 'handed' the same as the other house of the pair. If in fact the variation was overlooked when the front door was ordered and fitted, the only difference you would probably notice is that you may have some difficulty getting into the house because the door opens the wrong way, and when you are in you can't find the light switch because it's behind the door.

A simple error in setting-out can result in a house being built back-to-front and I have known this happen. However, there are some housing estates where the houses are deliberately built with the rear elevations fronting on the main estate roads, whilst the fronts are located in cul-de-sacs at the rear. The original purpose was probably to save some money on the layout of the drainage, but the lasting effect is confusion; the houses that are apparently in Smith Avenue have a postal address in Jones Close, and Smith Avenue is 'fronted' by a line of rear elevations and back gardens.

Terraces of houses can be built with numerous combinations of right- and left-hand houses. On one housing site I dealt with there was terrace of some 20 houses. The brickie who set out the front elevation failed to notice that the second house along was handed. He also proceeded to set out the window and door openings of each house from the preceding one instead of individually. Thus every house following the handed one had its doors and windows on the ground floor in the wrong position. He didn't notice his error until he reached the nineteenth house – which was also handed. Detached houses can also be built 'as drawing' or 'handed' or 'turned 90°', that is with the front entrance door at the side. If you live in a detached house with its front entrance door at the side and unpleasantly close to your neighbour, whilst on the opposite side of your house you have an enormously spacious corner plot garden, then it's a fair bet that your house was supposed to be turned 90° and handed but that the handing was overlooked until it was too late.

Handing is not limited to houses. The drawings for large buildings often contain instructions such as 'west wing as east wing but handed'; or 'block B as block A but handed'; or 'sixth floor toilets as fifth floor but handed'. This last instruction would be quite diabolical because it could probably be interpreted in two or three different ways. Provided the ambiguity is realised in time, no great harm would be done because the Contractor would raise a query. The trouble with ambiguities is that they are often not seen as such until the Architect comes along after the work is done and says, 'That wasn't what I meant. Surely it's quite clear that I meant...'

Various fittings and components that go into a building also have to be made right or left handed. I mentioned sink tops that require specifying to indicate which side the draining board is on. Windows and doors can be hung either hand. In addition, doors can be hung to open inward or outward – another complication and another opportunity for error.

With the windows and doors go the ironmongery, that is the various locks, fasteners, handles etc. Many of these items are reversible; the handing can be reversed by the simple expedient of turning them up the other way. But with many locks, latches and closers this is not possible. Great efforts have been made to standardise descriptions particularly with the advent of the single European Market. Previously what one manufacturer designated a left-hand lock might have been designated a right-hand lock by another; whilst many Architects had their own pet methods of definition.

One tall office building that I was involved with was planned in a T-shape and the main staircase and lifts were at the junction of the T. There were expensive, glazed, hardwood doors with glazed-screen sidelights at the entrance to each of the three wings. The Site Agent prepared a very detailed joinery and ironmongery schedule. It was only when the doors and screens were manufactured and delivered that he found, to his horror, that by virtue of a simple error on the schedule, the doors as they were made would open inwards instead of outwards.

His heart sank until he realised that the doors and screens were symmetrical. Great! All he had to do was to turn the whole thing round so that the doors would open out. He was happy and could breathe again – until the Glazier appeared on site.

'Just a small query.'

'Yes?'

'Those big screens at each floor on the main stairs.'

'yes?'

'Shouldn't the glazing beads be on the inside?'

'Why?'

'Well, they're screw beads. Any bugger with a screwdriver could get in in about two minutes flat just by unscrewing the beads and taking out a pane of glass.'

It was true. There were expensive security locks on the doors. The glass was wired, polished plate for security and fire resistance. And yet any intruder with a screwdriver could gain access in no time at all. At great expense all the doors and screens had to be reversed again and altered.

22

Round the Bend with a Gooley

The first building site I ever worked on was in West London in 1943 The war was still on. The main building was an existing factory that had employed all-male workers before the war. During the war many of the employees were female, and the female toilet facilities were quite inadequate. We were building an extension that comprised 48 female toilets.

I was the junior member of the organisation. I helped with anything and everything: wages, time-keeping, records, getting the Foreman's daily ounce of Cut Golden Bar tobacco or any other errands. I was very bashful and shy of girls, and was often detailed to go into the factory where many of the teenage girls were working. With hindsight I think this was arranged on purpose. As it was nothing very untoward ever happened to me, but looking back on it, it was probably just as well I was so naive and had no inkling of the danger I was in. I have since heard of quite horrendous tales involving red paint being daubed in all sorts of private places by young girls in similar circumstances; or milk bottles being used for quite unmentionable rites. I would have died with embarrassment. Fortunately for me it never happened!

I did get caught for one embarrassing mission however. Again in my sweet innocence I didn't realise what I had been let in for until it was too late.

'We've broken an S-trap pan, so I want you to go and get a replacement.'

'Where from?'

'Fulham.'

I had no idea what an S-trap pan was. Fulham was about 10 miles away, about an hour on public transport. I duly travelled to the builders merchant in Fulham and presented the site order. I was given the S-trap pan, which I saw to my horror was a toilet pan. I tucked it under my arm, my fingers literally round the bend. I walked to the bus stop; waited. Got on the bus to Hammersmith; walked into the tube station. Got the train to Ealing; walked to the bus stop; waited. Got on the bus to Perivale; walked to the site.

All of this time I was *praying* that I would not meet anyone I knew. I didn't, but can you imagine what it was like on the train standing there with a toilet pan next to me, or on the bus the comments I had from the conductor, not to mention the passengers.

The ganger man on the job was a tall, thin fellow known as Scotty. He had a genial sense of humour but his main claim to fame was that apparently he only had one testicle. I don't know

whether he lost one or was only born with one but he wasn't bothered about it. In fact, he told most people about it and was proud of the fact that he had three children.

Like many ganger men, Scotty was not very literate. I don't say this unkindly or in any mocking way. I am sure I would make a worse job of laying concrete than Scotty ever made of filling in a form or writing a labour allocation sheet. Scotty wrote as he spoke and that was that. On one occasion he had to write a brief report of an accident in the accident book. What had actually happened was this: one of the labourers was attempting to start the concrete mixer by winding the starting handle. The handle had come out and had struck the poor chap in the groin.

Scotty's report of the incident read: '... was winding the mixer when handle came out and hit left bollock'. This caused great amusement everywhere, not so much because of Scotty's lack of the use of the correct medical terminology, but because he had particularised on the fact that it was the *left* one.

23

T&P

It's amazing how many recollections over the years are associated with either tea or toilets or both. When you think about it there is a sort of logical progression there, but that wasn't quite what I had in mind.

Site tea is legendary. As a generalisation I think it has improved over the years. This might come as a surprise to those of a comparatively tender age who endure contemporary brews. I like plenty of sugar with my tea, so I can effectively disguise the taste. But to those masochists who insist that they actually want to taste the tea, it must generally be grim.

Many years ago I had several jobs to visit each month in South Wales. I have wonderful memories of slag heaps, the Mumbles railway, the beautiful countryside and beaches of the Gower Peninsular, Singleton Park in Swansea and seeing Billy Cotton and Tessie O'Shea at the Swansea Empire. But my abiding memory is of the site tea. The war had been over for several years but tea was still rationed; I believe there was a small catering allowance for building sites. Nevertheless, either because the allowance was too small or because the full allowance wasn't all used for the intended purpose and was siphoned off to the black market, there never seemed to be enough.

Safety, health and welfare regulations were not really in force and hygiene was scarcely known. Making the tea in a large pot or urn was also virtually unknown; generally it was made in a bucket over a gas ring. The tea leaves themselves had to be conserved and were actually only thrown away at the end of the week! With luck the week started with some fresh leaves in the bucket on Monday morning. These were added to on Monday afternoon and further supplemented on each succeeding day. The taste was absolutely disgusting. Connoisseurs could probably have guessed the day of the week by the taste which deteriorated by the day. What the effect was on the stomach lining can only be imagined.

*

Things had marginally improved a few years later when I was the Project Quantity Surveyor on a large office building job in the City of London. Tea was no longer rationed but the taste of the site tea left as much to be desired as ever, to say the least. The tea man was a short podgy fellow in his fifties with a face resembling a garden gnome. The resemblance was enhanced by the fact that he had a slight hunchback. Unfortunately making the tea was only his secondary occupation.

Although, as I say, several years had elapsed since my regular visits to South Wales such safety, health and welfare regulations as there were, were treated rather scantily. Toilet facilities on construction sites are luxurious today compared with what they used to be. I may have some more to say on this later. For the moment, suffice to say that the facilities provided in those days were spartan! Apart from a few chemical closets at ground level the 'facilities' consisted of buckets placed at strategic points around the building! I need hardly add that at that time there were no female site employees.

Bear in mind that 'the building' was incomplete – in this case it was a reinforced-concrete framed building. The frame, including the concrete floors, was erected first and the brick or stone 'cladding' was constructed afterwards. This meant that before the 'cladding' was added there were no external walls. The upper floors were open to the elements and, barring the odd column or small concrete wall, were visible to the populace at large –

Unfortunately making the tea was only his secondary occupation.

including quite often the strategically placed buckets. As the job progressed, and the cladding was built and internal partitions were erected, a degree of privacy was possible. But of course as the job progressed, so the labour force increased, as did the number of buckets that required emptying – by the little garden gnome.

It was a full-time job – well almost! Every bucket had to be transported from wherever it was to ground-floor level to be emptied and taken back up again. A full-time job – except for half an hour mid-morning and half an hour mid-afternoon when the gnome took time out to make the tea!

24

All's Well that Ends Well

They say all men are boys at heart. Whether or not that is true, certainly, in my experience a high proportion of Quantity Surveyors have an impish sense of humour, particularly those whose work base is actually out on a construction site. Out of sight of the Firm's top brass, there is more scope for the occasional practical joke. I've instigated a few in my time and when I was a junior Surveyor was on the receiving end more than once.

I fell for the old chestnut when I was sent to the local iron-monger to get a dozen bolt holes. The old fellow behind the counter in his long brown overall looked over his half-moon glasses and said, 'I think someone's been having you on lad.' And so they had. I thought bolt holes were the things you set into a floor that bolts went into. They are actually called bolt sockets but bolt holes seemed logical enough to me.

The next week they tried to get me to go to the local chemist for two packets of Durex. I didn't know what Durex was but I was highly suspicious and after the episode of the bolt holes I refused to go.

*

These days smoking is considered anti-social and passive smoking, that is breathing the smoke from other people's cigarettes, is considered almost as harmful as smoking itself. In a 10-foot-square site hut housing three Surveyors it must be harmful and can be quite unpleasant if even just one of the three smokes.

This was the situation on a site where one of my two assistants smoked a pipe. It was really awful. He kept his tobacco in a leather pouch, which he often left lying on his desk. One day after I sent him out on site on some pretext we laced his tobacco with wood shavings from the pencil sharpener. He duly came back, lit up and puffed away merrily as if nothing had happened. The only reaction we got was about three hours later when he casually commented 'God, my mouth feels a bit dry today.'

*

At one time quite elaborate precautions were taken on large sites to prevent men clocking in, and then slipping away to clock in at another site down the road. Most employees, other than very specialised tradesmen, were directly employed at that time, rather than self-employed as they are frequently nowadays. Neither were they employed by Subcontractors. Two or three times each day the timekeeper, or someone from the wages office, would go round the site and ask every man he met his check number. He would mark off all the numbers in his book and any man whose number was not checked off would have to explain where he was and get confirmation from the Ganger or section Foreman.

The odd thing was that the timekeepers rarely looked at any man's face when they checked off the numbers. Thus it often happened that my assistants or I – who walked round the site in old trousers, donkey jackets and rubber boots – often got the tap on the shoulder and 'What's your number?' The instinctive reaction of 'piss off !' was rather risky since the timekeepers were usually chosen for their brawn rather than their brains. In any case it was much more fun simply to rap back the first number that came into your head and rapidly disappear.

'What's your number?'

'34'

'I've had 34'

101

'Oh, sorry – 44'

'I've had 44'

'Well you asked me before.'

'Are you sure?'

'Look, do you think I don't know my own number?'

'Oh, it's you!'

Of course if he hadn't had 34 or 44 before he would mark them off in the book and the real fireworks started when he tapped the navvy on the shoulder whose number really was 34 or 44.

*

One innocent practical joke I played could have ended in tragedy.

The General Foreman was a 'car' man. His car was a status symbol but he hadn't graduated to being given a Company car to use. He was very proud that he had his own car and had just purchased a brand new Vauxhall Cresta: highly polished, gleaming black and chrome and, in the then current vogue, featured very prominent rear tail fins, which housed the rear lights, covered with large plastic lenses a foot or more in height.

He had had the car for only a matter of days when someone ran into the back of him. The damage wasn't too severe and was limited to the near-side tail fin. The rear light assembly was damaged including the red perspex lens, part of which was missing whilst the remainder was still hanging on the chrome screws.

The Foreman never risked parking the car in the car park, preferring to leave it next to the site offices. Sometimes it was parked just outside my window. A day or two after the damage had occurred and whilst the Foreman was out on site I nipped out, unscrewed the red perspex cover to the off-side rear light assembly and replaced it with parts of the broken plastic from the near-side assembly. To the passing observer it now appeared that both rear lights had been damaged.

A little while later when the Foreman returned I casually said to him, 'Didn't you say it was the near side of your car, which was damaged?'

'That's right.'

'Well, your off-side rear light's broken as well now, you must have had a second knock.'

'You're joking!'

'No, have a look.'

He did have a look and immediately ran outside. When he reached the car he literally went purple in the face and started jumping up and down with rage. I really thought he was going to have a heart attack. Only when I gently waved the intact offside red plastic lens, which I had removed, at him did he gradually realise that he had been had.

'You bastard,' he shouted at me. But he was so relieved to see that his precious car had not really been damaged any further that he quickly recovered his composure and the coronary was avoided.

The car was fated however because a few weeks later, after the damage had been repaired, the Foreman was out driving it when he bent down to retrieve something from the floor. He didn't bother to stop and as the road curved to the right he uprooted a lamp post with the near-side front end of the car. Fortunately, he wasn't injured, apart from by way of his pride.

25

The Little Dog Laughed

I am very fond of animals, particularly dogs. Strange dogs come up to me to be fondled and fussed, and I have never been bitten. Cats on the other hand, until quite recently, treated me with disdain.

A few years ago I was asked by a prospective buyer to carry out a survey and inspection of a bungalow he was thinking of purchasing. The owner was expecting me. When I rang the doorbell there was a short burst of heavy breathing followed by a thunderous crash against the front door, accompanied by barks, snarls and growls.

The lady of the house opened the door a couple of inches. I explained the purpose of my visit and suggested that perhaps she might like to let the dog – a Doberman – into the back garden before I came in. She duly did so and I proceeded with my inspection. The dog, however, was not to be outdone. Every time he glimpsed me through the kitchen door, the patio doors or a window, he hurled himself with a crash towards me. He would surely have torn me apart had he got at me.

The time came for me to go outside to inspect the rear of the house. Again, at my suggestion the dog was brought indoors before I went into the back garden. The previous performance was repeated. Every time I passed a glazed door or window there was a monstrous crash as the brute charged against it.

When I had finished I walked round to the front of the house intending to knock at the front door to advise the lady occupant that I was leaving. The front door was open. No one was to be seen. I edged inside. 'Hello.' I called. No response. I edged a bit further and a bit further. Then I froze. There, standing in the middle of the lounge and looking straight at me, was the Doberman. 'If I move, he'll have me' I thought. I stood absolutely still and for a minute or two we eyed one another. Slowly I crouched down and extended my hand towards him. 'Come on boy, come on.' Slowly he edged towards me as I coaxed him. He sniffed my fingers for a few seconds and I tickled his chin and began to fondle him. Five minutes later the owner appeared and was dumbfounded to see me sitting on the floor with her dog making a great fuss of me. If dogs could laugh I am sure he would have been laughing at the fright he had given me. As it was he wouldn't stop slobbering over me whilst his mistress offered me tea and biscuits.

*

Whether or not he was laughing in the end I know not, but grimacing was probably a more apt description for the expression on his face at one point. I am now referring to a bull mastiff who befriended me during my fortnightly visits to a job at picturesque Symonds Yat near Ross-on-Wye.

One of the labourers on the job bred bull mastiffs as a hobby. I happened to mention him to the landlady of the hotel I stayed at on my visits and, quite early in the job, she bought a puppy from him. As the job progressed so did the pup. He used to recognise me as I parked my car and come bounding towards me. When he was full grown he weighed over 100 pounds, and almost knocked me over in his enthusiasm to greet me.

Symonds Yat is a tourist spot during the summer but during the winter months I was often the only resident guest in the hotel. The dog used to follow me about and I used to take him for walks. When I sat in splendid isolation in the hotel dining room he used to come and sit alongside me waiting for tit bits. One day he

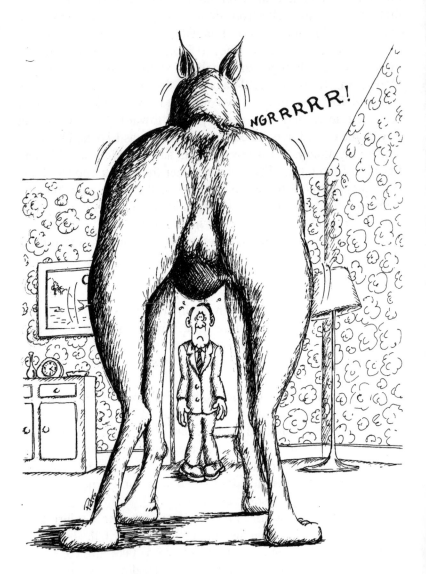

'If I move, he'll have me,' I thought.

suddenly starting bounding backwards and forwards between my table and the door to the terrace. He even started barking 'Shut up you fool,' I said to him.

But with hindsight I was the fool for not understanding the very clear message he was trying to get across. He did shut up, but when I next looked at him there he was squatting between the tables beautifully laid out for the evening's visitors, depositing a pile of you-know-what in the middle of the restaurant. It would have made a hilarious photograph. I took the coward's way out and said not a word to the landlady. Perhaps that made the dog laugh.

26

The Penis Mightier Than the Sword

Don McCoughan was a house salesman; that is to say, he was the representative of a developer who built and sold houses. As his name implies, he was Scottish. In fact he hailed from Glasgow and had a face that had all the appearance of having been hewn from Scottish granite. He was about 5'6" tall, of slim, wiry build. He certainly had a good sense of humour and he was in no way inhibited by his lack of stature – particularly with the fairer sex whom he frequently indecently assaulted in one way or another.

Don had an artistic turn of mind, with a talent for interior design and furnishing. This combined with his 'gift of the gab' made him a first-class house salesman. The Firm generally erected a show area on each of the sites, with at least one of the dwellings fully decorated and furnished. Don designed the decor and selected the furnishings. More than once the master bedroom was furnished with a four-poster bed, 'Very sexy,' he would say, 'Just watch their knees buckle when they see that.'

Four-posted or straightforward double bed, every show bedroom was equipped with bedside cabinets, and the drawer of every bedside cabinet contained a packet of condoms. Whether their knees buckled or not, it really was a study in psychology to watch the reactions of the potential female customers who, as they walked around, would *always*, or so it seemed, casually and inquisitively open the drawers. Some would blush and shut the drawer quickly pretending they hadn't noticed, others would suppress a giggle. If Don was anywhere nearby he would remark that 'our houses are fitted with *everything*'. Out of earshot of the husband he would probably offer his services to prove it.

He was fairly liberal with his offers. In fact it was quite embarrassing going into a department store with him. Those with furnishing departments all knew him. Virtually any female assistant was fair game for his bawdy comments. 'Ah, your behuchi's looking good today. Behuchi is Glaswegian for bottom. 'Did you get a bit last night then?'

'No.'

'D'ye want a bit tonight?' He was very rarely rebuffed.

Tammy, a girl in the sales department in the area office, was one of Don's regulars (as indeed it appeared were most of the saleswomen on the sites, although it was one of his complaints that the Firm's policy seemed to be to employ salesmen rather than saleswomen generally). Tammy and Don had an unfortunate mishap one warm, sunny day.

On some pretext Tammy was out with Don in his car. They decided that a grassed bank to the local canal was a nice secluded spot for a 'short break'. They duly drove off the road, parked the car on the bank and proceeded to indulge themselves. The bank sloped up from the road and nearby footpath and then gently down to the water's edge, concealing them from any prying eyes. Unfortunately – very unfortunately – Don omitted to leave the car in gear and the handbrake failed to hold it. Slowly, imperceptibly and unnoticed by the lovers, the vehicle rolled down the slope and into the water.

Such was the camaraderie in the department, from the Departmental Manager downwards, that a mobile crane was despatched from the Firm's yard in quick time, together with a transporter, and the car was back on the road in a couple of days – and no one outside the department was any the wiser.

On the subject of Don's stature it was one of his boasts that his modest physique was not that modest anyway. 'I take size nine in shoes,' he would tell you, 'and you know what they say about little men with big feet. I'm plenty big enough where it matters. In fact if the social club ever hold a fancy dress dance, I'm going to put it in my ear and come as a petrol pump!'

27

Top Heavy at the Front

Most construction contracts provide for the Contractor to receive an interim payment every month. On a very large project it might even be every fortnight. This means that every month the work completed has to be valued. On a building contract that would be the job of the Client's Quantity Surveyor (the PQS). On a civil engineering contract the chore would fall to the Client's Engineer, who in practice might well employ a Quantity Surveyor. Whether it is a building or civil engineering contract, the situation is broadly similar so, for the purpose of illustration, I will take a building contract.

The object of the valuation is purely to enable an interim payment to be made. The fact that the payment has been made does not generally carry with it any implication that the work has been carried out correctly. Normally it is not the function of the PQS to certify that work is in accordance with the specification – that is down to the Contract Administrator. Nevertheless, it goes without saying that the PQS will only include in his valuation such work that has at least the appearance of being correctly carried out.

The valuation is not intended to be exact; indeed that would be quite impossible. Many of the items of work being valued will be in a partially finished state when it is prepared. For example, drain trenches may still be open with the pipes unjointed in them; or only the backing coat of plaster-work may have been executed, leaving the finishing coat still to be applied.

Quite apart from all this, work continues to progress whilst the actual valuation is being prepared. The Surveyor may take half a day or a day going around the site making his notes on the stage of progress reached. On even quite a modest-sized contract some £8,000–£10,000 worth of work may be done each day, so to attempt to evaluate the work down to the last pound would clearly be quite pointless.

When the Surveyor has completed his valuation, depending on the procedure laid down in the contract, he either issues a certificate detailing the value of the work or he sends the figures to the Contract Administrator with his recommendation as to the amount the Administrator should certify. The certificate, when it is issued, is sent to the Contractor and the Client, who has to pay the Contractor the amount certified within a specified number of days. Under some contracts the count of days does not begin until the Contractor has formally 'presented' the certificate to his Client.

By the time the PQS has completed his valuation and sent his figures to the Administrator; and by the time the Administrator has sent the certificate to the Contractor; and by the time the Contractor has presented it to the Client, quite a few days may well have elapsed before the count of days begins. During all this time the Contractor is carrying out more work and financing the project. If, during that time, the Client were to go bankrupt all that funding would be lost.

Conversely, if just after the Client had made an interim payment the Contractor went bankrupt, not only would work come to a halt but another Contractor would have to be found to complete the job. The replacement Firm's prices would almost certainly be more than those of the original Contractor. Even if there is an insurance bond in place to cover this eventuality, it would be in the Client's interest to have as much money 'in hand' as possible. The interests of the Contract Administrator and the PQS lie in the same direction because the last possible thing that they want is to find – after a Contractor has gone bankrupt – that he has been overpaid.

So to avoid this happening, the professional team will tend to 'sit on' the paperwork as long as possible or even to deliberately under-certify the value of work done. Rumour has it that in some cases, during periods of high interest rates, this has been actively encouraged by some Clients. Of course no one will ever admit to doing such a thing – the very idea!

Meanwhile the interests of the Contractor lie in precisely the opposite direction. He wants the valuation to be as high as possible and for the paperwork to be processed as rapidly as possible.

The Contractor's Surveyor has, in any case, to prepare a very much more detailed valuation than that required for the purpose of an interim payment and cash flow. The Contractor needs to know whether or not his job is making a profit. After all that is why he is in business. So what ensues is a somewhat convoluted arrangement part of which could again be described as a 'professional fiddle'. The Contractor's Surveyor will be required to prepare his detailed valuation up to a specific date in the calendar month, normally to coincide with or fit in with the Firm's accounting procedures. The specific date could be the end of the month, the middle of the month or perhaps the last weekend in the month. It does not really matter so long as the clearing of invoices, stocktaking of unfixed materials on the site, as well as the Surveyor's valuation, are all carried out effectively on the same date. This will enable a reasonable reconciliation to be made of various materials used with the Surveyor's measurements.

The Surveyor will then endeavour to base his application for payment – his 'external' valuation – on his detailed 'internal' valuation. The PQS is generally only too happy to do this since it can save him quite a lot of work for which he, or at least his Firm, are receiving a fee from the Client – hence the 'professional fiddle'. The only problem that looms as far as the PQS is concerned is that as I have said, the last thing he wants to do is to over-value the interim payment for fear the Contractor goes bankrupt. But he knows full well that the Contractor's Surveyor will almost certainly try to inflate the valuation if possible.

This juggling with the figures produces something of a haggle about dates early on. If the Contractor is entitled to his first payment one month after commencing work on the site he would like to receive the actual cash at that time. However, this might not be practicable because of the administrative time required to process the valuation as well as the usual contractual requirement that the Client does not have to pay the money for perhaps ten or fourteen days after receiving the certificate.

The PQS will try to delay the preparation of the first valuations, because this will set the timetable for all the subsequent ones. On the other hand, the Contractor's Surveyor has the problem of bringing the date forward as far as possible, consistent with the fact that he will want to relate his 'external' valuation to his 'internal' figures which are – hopefully – much more accurate. If he has his 'accurate' figures completed when he prepares his 'external' valuation he has a norm on which he can build.

From time to time a diligent PQS will appear who insists that *he* will prepare the interim valuation. This will cause some problems for the Contractor's Surveyor because the PQS's valuation will be virtually useless for the requirements of the Contractor's Surveyor. It will have insufficient detail and the date on which the PQS prepares it may be incompatible with the Contractor's accounting procedures. The 'internal' and 'external' valuations have to be reconciled with one another so far as the Contractor is concerned. In this respect the Contractor's Surveyor is in the 'hot seat'.

If the 'external' valuation is low but at the same time the Surveyor's 'internal' figures show that the job is making a profit, it may appear that the Surveyor has inflated the 'internal' figures for the sake of an easy life. When he insists this is not the case he will get more flak because he may then be accused of 'not getting the money in', thereby causing his Firm to use more finance than necessary to fund the job.

On the other hand if the 'internal' valuation, indicates that the job is making a loss, or not making as much profit as it should, whilst at the same time the cashflow situation based on the 'external' valuation is good, the Surveyor may be accused of under-valuing the job for his 'internal' valuation perhaps so that he can later demonstrate what a clever chap he is by turning the job round and converting the loss incurred on the site into a profit derived from his measurement and negotiating skills. The best way to avoid this type of recrimination developing is for the Surveyor to have a positive function in the management of the job. This does indeed happen much more frequently than used to be the case.

If all this talk of 'internal' and 'external' valuations sounds complicated, believe me it is. Indeed there is another very complicated aspect with which many Contractor's Surveyors have to cope: the very dubious practice of what is generally known as 'front-loading'.

Front-loading in principle is quite straightforward. In practice it can become very complicated for the Contractor's Surveyor. The object of the exercise is to enable the Contractor to obtain monies before he is truly entitled to them. Thus for example, work that will be carried out early in the job will be overpriced at tender stage at the expense of work that will be carried out later. This operation involves the estimating department in a lot of very hurried work.

To begin with the job has to be priced correctly. If the tender submitted is amongst the lowest, the detailed priced Bills of Quantities will be called for by the PQS and will be required within 24 or 48 hours. A frantic operation will then take place to amend the Bills, increasing the rates of, say, the foundation and basement works whilst reducing later items such as joinery and finishing trades by the equivalent amount of money. Some PQSs ask for all tendering firms to submit their detailed priced Bills of Quantities together with the tenders – perhaps in separate sealed envelopes. In those cases, if a front-loading exercise takes place it has to be carried out before the tender is submitted.

One of the objects of the PQS calling for the detailed prices is to establish that the Contractor has in fact priced the tender and not only simply taken a cover price from another firm tendering as I explained in Chapter 10. However, another reason for the PQS asking to see the Bills of Quantities is to enable him to examine the actual rates, so that he can verify that the tender has not been front-loaded. If front-loading has been achieved by juggling rates the PQS has a difficult task because every Contractor's rates vary in any event. There is no 'right answer' as to what a particular rate should be.

The PQS's task may be a bit easier if the front-loading has been achieved by using another method either entirely or in part. A significant part of a Contractor's tender consists of pricing what are known as 'Preliminaries'. These may comprise such items as scaffolding, cranes, overall supervision and the Contractor's general site set-up, including his temporary offices. These are all usually listed in a section at the front of the Bills of Quantities, separate from the individual trades or work sections.

There is no obligation on the Contractor to price the Preliminaries separately, although most Contractors do so to a greater or lesser degree. Each Contractor has his own method, for example, some Contractors may regard their tower cranes as being required mainly for the structural framework of the building. They may 'spread' the cost of the cranes over each cubic metre of concrete or tonne of steel in the framework, rather than include the cost in the Preliminaries.

Preliminaries divide naturally into three categories: lump-sum items, such as the installation and removal of the temporary site offices or scaffolding; time-based items, such as the weekly hire charges for the offices or scaffolding; and percentage or proportionate items, which relate directly to the value or volume of the works, such as insurance premiums.

Some Contractors put part or all of their total profit element of the job into the Preliminaries, adding it into the set-up or time-based items. If this is not queried by the PQS when he examines the detailed tenders, the effect will be that the Contractor will be paid a significant portion of his profit margin for the whole job very early on and before he has actually carried out the work to which the profit relates.

Any element of 'front-loading' or over-valuation *must* be adjusted by the Contractor's Surveyor when he prepares his 'internal' valuation. If he does not, the job will appear to be making a handsome profit when in fact it may be doing nothing of the kind. This will engender a false sense of well-being amongst everyone concerned. Controls on expenditure will tend to be relaxed and the general situation that will prevail will truly be a calm before the storm. As the job proceeds the over-valuation will gradually be corrected. The profit the job was thought to be making will evaporate and, too late, the job will be seen to be making a loss and the recriminations will begin.

*

'Front-loading' can have quite disastrous consequences, either accidentally or perhaps quite intentionally. I can quote two examples.

A Contractor from small beginnings had expanded to a significant size with an increasing annual turnover. He made a habit of front-loading his tenders and the practice had apparently gone largely unnoticed by his various Clientele and their respective Quantity Surveyors.

Initially the result of the front-loading reduced his bank over-draft and put him into a good cash position. The cash position on front-loaded jobs deteriorates as they progress and the later under-priced sections of the work have to be carried out. This can be overcome, as it was in this instance, by obtaining more work similarly front-loaded and allowing the influx of cash from the new job or jobs to finance the completion of the existing ones. Eventually a recession loomed and the supply of new jobs dried up. Suddenly there was no finance available to complete the various contracts in hand and the Contractor was forced into liquidation. Effectively the Contractor had been overpaid on most, if not all of the incomplete Contracts, and the unfortunate Clientele were left to pick up the tabs.

In the second example the effect of the front-loading was exacerbated by the negligence of the Client's Surveyor, the PQS.

The Contract was a large Local Authority housing project; the Contractor, a small, private, limited Company. Each month when a valuation was due the Contractor prepared all the paperwork, including the charts that graphically indicated the state of progress of the various works in all the houses and flats. I had nothing to do with the job at that time but was told by a number of individuals that the PQS used to meet the Contractor's Managing Director briefly each month to be given the requisite paperwork. I was told he never went into any of the dwellings, indeed on some occasions he did not even get out of his car.

Suddenly, immediately after clearing a cheque for an interim payment, the Contractor folded. His office was closed, the Managing Director nowhere to be found. I was employed to look into the matter. I found that the works had been over-valued, and the Contractor consequently overpaid by the present-day equivalent of a sum approaching £500,000.

The PQS was a large Firm. Their employee, who had been dealing with the job, was transferred at short notice to the Far East, amid suspicion of corruption. The fact that his car was an expensive sports model and that he invariably wore expensive suits was apparently explained by the fact that he had no family and that his wife also had a very highly paid job.

I examined the Contractor's prices and was convinced that the pricing was front-loaded. I also found that numerous items of work included in the valuations had not actually been carried out or their value had been exaggerated. I reported my findings and was threatened with a libel suit by the PQS. It never materialised.

Subsequently I played no further part in the saga so I have no idea how it was concluded. However, I was in no doubt that the Contractor was on the Hey Diddle Diddle with a vengeance; possibly the PQS's employee as well.

118

28

Cooking the Books

Not all fiddles are carried out by Employees; some are operated by Employers I have mentioned Subcontractors and Suppliers' proprietors who attempt to coerce the Contractors' Employees. If they succeed, the dishonesty involves both Employers and Employees. However, on occasion only the Main Contractor may be involved. If it is a small Firm it might be the Proprietor who organises the scam; if it is a larger Company it could be one or more of a number of Directors or possibly senior staff carrying out their bidding.

When I was a very junior site Surveyor I remember the big white chief visiting the site one day when some concrete floor slabs were being poured. 'How thick are these slabs supposed to be?' he asked. 'Six inches,' he was told. All hell broke loose when he measured the thickness and found they were indeed six inches. 'If the specification says six inches you don't put them in more than five and a half at the most,' he blasted at the Foreman.

That big white chief was many years later knighted, I believe, for his services to the Construction Industry!

His attitude permeated down the line. On another site I was on with the same Firm, much of the work was being paid for on a 'cost-plus' basis. That is, the Contractor was paid a set percentage of profit on top of his incurred costs. He simply had to produce time sheets, invoices and the like to substantiate them.

Well that was no problem because, unbeknown to many people

119

outside the Company, one of the main plant hire Firms from whom much of the machinery on the site was hired was in fact a subsidiary. Obtaining invoices to justify costs allegedly incurred presented no difficulty at all. The costs allegedly incurred were recorded on weekly time sheets all of which were signed – wittingly or unwittingly – by a Clerk of Works. The invoices were then prepared from the time sheets.

*

Groundworks or large earthworks jobs lent themselves to a fiddle. For example, if below-ground obstructions such as rock or concrete are encountered they have to be removed. They should be recorded, but frequently the records are not too meticulously prepared because by the time they are referred to the obstructions are gone and nothing can be checked. 'Soft spots', that is pockets of soft ground that have to be removed and replaced with concrete or hardcore such as broken bricks, provided another example of records which cannot subsequently be verified.

*

It is essential at the commencement of a new job for a grid of the site levels to be prepared and agreed, providing a record of the level of the site before work begins. Thus when ground has to be excavated it is possible to calculate the volume of excavation by working out the difference between the ground levels before and after the work is carried out. Similarly, if the ground has to be 'made up' or filled, it is possible to calculate the volume of fill material.

In an area where the ground has to be excavated or 'cut,' it is to the Contractor's advantage to agree the original levels as high as possible to maximise the volume of excavation. In a 'fill' area the reverse is true. Thus agreeing an original grid of levels is quite a skilled operation. The ground does not undulate like a line on a drawing. There are localised bumps and crannies and even the most honest Engineer has to be careful that he sites the levelling staff on a spot that is reasonably representative of the terrain nearby. On a large site to be consistently too high or low can make a substantial difference.

The best advice I can give anyone preparing a grid of levels is to be as accurate as possible. Quite apart from the doubtful ethics of trying to 'cook' the levels there is always the risk that they can be cooked the wrong way. An Engineer once came to me with the level grid he had just completed and pronounced that he had done well with it. 'I had the staff on the toe of my boot every time,' he said. That meant that all the levels were about 75 mm (3″) high.

'Well done,' I said with heavy sarcasm. 'You realise you were in a fill area? You've just lost us 75 mm of fill over the whole of that part of the site.'

'Cooking' the levels in that way is virtually undetectable at a later date. If the Surveyor working out the quantities of cut and fill certifies payments to a Subcontractor or Supplier using the false levels and then uses the same levels as the basis for the payments the Main Contractor is to receive, he can truly say that the falsifying of the records has cost his Employer (the Main Contractor) nothing. Any overpayment to the Subcontractor or Supplier has been recovered from the Client. The Client will normally remain blissfully unaware of what is going on, as indeed may the Surveyor's Employer.

If in fact the Surveyor's Employer *is* aware of what is happening he would appear at first sight to be gaining nothing out of the fiddle. In practice his gain would be in the form of unduly low or uneconomical prices he would be paying to the Subcontractor or Supplier. The prices would only become economical to the Subcontractor or Supplier by virtue of the inflated quantities.

This sort of situation was illustrated in practice in connection with a site operated by one Firm I worked for. I was not working on the site concerned and so do not know all the details at first hand and cannot vouch for their exact authenticity. However, I felt the ramifictions as did all the other Surveyors with the Firm.

*

Some large Firms in the Construction Industry employ what they euphemistically refer to as 'detectives'. These are individuals employed to safeguard against fiddling. Every now and then they uncover a scam. In this particular instance they uncovered it quite by accident.

A site Project Surveyor on a large earthworks contract apparently had some domestic problems and decided to depart without notice. He had been provided with a Company car, which he left locked on the site when he departed. A Mechanic was detailed to visit the site and bring the car back to the local depot where a bank paying-in book belonging to the Surveyor was found in the glove compartment. The records showed that he had made weekly cash payments into his bank account substantially greater than the amount of his salary. Red lights flashed in high places. The Surveyor was eventually traced and it was found that he had received the weekly payments from the Firm supplying the fill material for the site. That Firm was being paid – or rather overpaid – on a measured basis identical to that on which the Main Contractor was being paid.

The Surveyor pleaded that his Employer had lost nothing, which was probably true. Nevertheless, a criminal prosecution was brought and the Surveyor went to jail for four years. The ramifications involved all so-called checking and verification procedures being tightened up – for a few months at least.

29

Issabuggerennit!

Some 'errors' are the result of particular working methods rather than actual mistakes. This was the case with another aspect of the job where the building was T-shaped and involved the glazed screens. In addition to the central staircase at the junction of the T, there were three other staircases, one at each extremity.

In addition to the difficulties in ensuring that a building and its components are built in the right place on the plan, they have to be built at the right level. Minor errors in levels are quite common. It is in fact almost impossible to build a structure at exactly the right level, or even precisely horizontally level. Nothing is actually physically impossible, but to attain exact precision of levels is not only unnecessary but would be enormously expensive. So there is always a degree of tolerance.

A finer degree of tolerance is required for the floor finishes, such as tiling or carpeting, than can be attained by the pouring of concrete. The fine tolerance required to receive the finishes is achieved either by hand-laying a screed mixture of cement and sand on top of the concrete or – nowadays more commonly – by power floating the concrete. Power floating leaves a smooth, hard and – hopefully – level surface to the concrete of sufficient accuracy to receive the floor finishes.

Pouring concrete staircases to the correct levels is even more difficult than pouring level slabs. The steps have to be set out very accurately and the construction of the moulds to receive the liquid concrete is a skilled operation. Some carpenters specialise in doing this and are often referred to as staircase hands. Even so, the concrete, when it is poured, may well not be sufficiently accurate to receive the final finish to the steps. Once again a cement/sand mixture may have to be laid to achieve the fine tolerance required. It is essential that all the risers on any one flight of finished stairs are virtually exactly equal.

On the T-shaped building the finish to the staircases was terrazzo. This consists of marble pieces laid into a coloured cement/sand mixture and ground and polished off to give an attractive and very hard-wearing finish. The specialist Firm doing the terrazzo decided to precast the finish to the stair treads and risers. The precast sections were L-shaped and their length coincided with the width of the staircase flights. Thus provided the concrete to the staircases was poured with reasonable accuracy, the terrazzo man anticipated that he would have little difficulty in setting his precast treads and risers to the correct levels. He obviously forgot Sod's Law. For whilst he decided it would be a good idea to precast his terrazzo treads and risers, the Main Contractor decided that because there were so many identical flights of concrete stairs it would be a good idea to precast them too. Like all good ideas this seemed a good one at the time.

To ensure the accuracy of the concrete steps, the flights were cast at ground level upside down. The moulds were made of the steps themselves and each whole flight was then to be lifted by the tower crane, turned over, hoisted and set into its final position.

The tower crane was located at the junction of the T, quite near to the main staircase. Apart from the physical difficulty of handling the stair flights so close to the crane's tower, the operation to place the flights to the main staircase went moderately well. The difficulties began when the flights to the staircases at the ends of the T were lifted.

The ends of the T were at the extreme range of the crane's capacity. Whilst the crane could lift 5 tonnes at its optimum distance, at extreme range its capacity was only 1 tonne. Some of the stair flights weighed 1½ tonnes. As soon as lifting commenced the overload bell started ringing.

The site Management decided to take the risk. 'Get 'em up and get 'em in fast' was the motto. Fortunately there were no accidents but needless to say the stair flights were not set in position with the greatest of accuracy. Not only were they frequently not at the correct level, they were not even at the correct gradient. The landings that were cast together with the flights were definitely not horizontal. In due course the terrazzo man had the task of setting his precast L-shaped treads and risers onto the precast concrete stair flights.

Terrazzo emanates from Italy and many terrazzo craftsmen are Italian. The Foreman on this job was an Italian, fifty or sixty years of age. He had a large walrus moustache and used to go around in a large black or dark-blue beret. He spoke halting English with a very strong Italian accent. As I came across him one morning he had just flung his beret to the ground and was muttering heavily accented English obscenities.

'What's the matter Luigi?'

'Hey looka dissa.'

'What?'

'Dissa ****ing staircase.'

'What's the matter with it?' I said tongue in cheek. Any fool could see what was the matter with it.

'Issabuggerennit!'

'What?'

'Issabugger! Issapissed!'

By this time I was having difficulty keeping a straight face. There might have been in international incident if I had laughed. 'What do you mean!'

'Looka. It start ata wrong place. Ita finish ata wrong place. Is all outa ****ing level. How I'ma supposed to do it. Is impossible.'

'No, nothing's impossible Luigi. There might be a bit of extra work involved but I'm sure you can fit it all in.'

'Ah! How? And who'sa gonna pay me for the extra ****ing work?'

'Well, *we'll* have to pay you otherwise you can't do it can you?'

As realisation dawned that there might be some extra money forthcoming he calmed down. Even so we had to lend him a couple of labourers with mechanical cutters to help him get over the problem, which he duly did – but at what cost!

30

Well, it Baffles Brains

As a general rule I find I dislike people who are 'personalities'. That is to say, people who set out to be extrovert. They try to dominate a conversation or make an entrance when they arrive. But some people are personalities without actually setting out to be so; they remain in your recollection long after you have met them, perhaps even long after they have died.

One such person was Mac, now sadly, I should think, long departed. He had already passed retiring age when I first met him and was a great one for name dropping. It was quite dangerous to mention a well-known personality because Mac had invariably met them – I suspect at a Masonic 'do' – and you would be regaled with stories about them for the next 15 or 20 minutes. Or even worse, he would pick up the telephone and try and contact them. On the odd occasion that he succeeded he would absolutely grovel to them.

Mac was a great groveller, especially to the boss. Basically he was a Quantity Surveyor. When I worked with him he was doing the estimating. Very often, he would also have to order the materials, something he wasn't really used to doing. Whatever he was like in his younger days I know not, but when I knew him his efficiency graph was definitely on a downward curve. His pricing cock-ups were only exceeded by his ordering cock-ups. Sometimes the latter resulted from the former. Be that as it may, I and the other younger members of staff got great amusement, not only in drawing his attention to his cock-ups, but also in watching the consummate way in which he attempted – sometimes not too successfully – to cover them up. Indeed, looking back on them, some of his cover-ups were doomed before they started.

For example, how could he possibly have realistically hoped to pass off black iron manhole covers and frames as galvanised simply by painting them with aluminium paint? That was what he tried to persuade the builders merchant to do when he discovered – too late – that he had ordered the wrong ones. The balloon went up when the builders merchant – an old crony of the boss – immediately phoned him and blew the gaff.

We were even more amused when we heard a site Foreman reporting to Mac that the 20-feet-wide by 10-feet-high steel sliding doors which Mac had ordered, had duly been delivered to site. But unfortunately they should have been 11 feet high. 'How's he going to get out of this?' we asked ourselves. Well he certainly tried, making various quite impractical suggestions en route. But as I recollect, the doors had to be scrapped and remade.

Mac had fought in France in the First World War and had experienced the poison gas that was used at that time. This had a lasting effect on his health, making him very chesty particularly during the winter. Not that this drew him much sympathy from the younger members of staff. Rather the reverse if anything and again amusement was the order of the day.

The offices we were using were converted from an old house; in fact we worked in what at one time were the bedrooms. Heating – such as it was – was by open coal fires and, being in former bedrooms, the fireplaces were rather small. Mac had the endearing habit of using the fireplace in his office to spit into – or rather to attempt to spit into because about four or five times out of ten he missed. 'Oh, God,' we would hear him say, and then look for a rapid excuse to burst in on him to cause the maximum embarrassment.

Eventually the Boss decided to install gas fires. This was a great improvement, although for purposes of economy the fires were not allowed to be lit until we arrived each morning. The first thing Mac did when he arrived was to turn on the gas. He didn't actually light it – that came later, much later. He took off his hat, coat, gloves, scarf etc., etc., dusted himself down, even on occasion went to the toilet. Then he tentatively offered up a lighted match to the fire. How he never caused any serious harm I'll never know. He frequently singed his right hand, which together with his wrist was quite bereft of hair.

I suppose one of the reasons that Mac grovelled to the Boss was that the Boss did have something of a short fuse to his temper, and he certainly didn't suffer fools gladly. But oddly enough when I joined the Firm I quickly found that one sure way to annoy him was to agree with him all the time. He much preferred you to argue with him than to agree with everything he said. Nevertheless, he did not like mistakes and because of his short fuse we would all go to great lengths to prevent them coming to light.

I have found over the years that almost all mistakes can be overcome, particularly if they are dealt with early enough. For that reason I have always impressed on staff and subordinates that the greatest 'crime' is not making mistakes – because we all make them at one time or another – but covering them up until they can only be rectified at great trouble and expense. Nevertheless, with a Boss like the one I am referring to it took great courage to confess to any error. He himself seemed to have an aura of infallibility. I can't actually remember him specifically making any mistakes. Perhaps because he never actually *did* anything, except write reams of letters and personally sign all orders for materials and subcontracts.

I suppose the nearest he came to a mistake was when he signed an order to a paint supplier for 5 gallons of flat-white paint. It should have read '5 gallons of flat white'. It actually read '5 gallons of flat shite' and the Boss signed the order without noticing the typing error. It only came to light when the site Foreman received his copy of the order the next day and 'phoned the office to ask, 'Do I put it on with a brush or a trowel?'

I came to realise the trepidation Mac must have experienced on discovering his cock-ups when I discovered one of my own. I was running a small site in Central London. The ground floor was a showroom that fronted on to Oxford Street and a side turning. There were plate glass windows along each frontage, although they were not display windows. In fact, they were to be obscured by sand-blasting the glass. This is quite an expensive process and the Architect decided that some money could be saved by utilising rough-cast plate glass – which is not transparent – instead of sand-blasting the expensive, polished plates of glass. He duly issued a variation order to effect the saving. Unfortunately I omitted to send a copy to the glazing Subcontractor.

I used to visit the site about twice each week. Three or four weeks later I arrived to find the hoardings dismantled to reveal the beautiful sandblasted, polished plate-glass windows that had been installed. My heart sank as immediately I remembered the variation order. 'This is it,' I thought, 'I'm for the chop.'

I could see no way out. I could not just do nothing. The Architect was bound to ask why we had ignored his instruction, and in any case the adverse cost involved was such that the mistake was bound to come to light. The next day I went in to see the Boss. 'I'm afraid I've dropped a clanger.'

'What have you done?'

I told him, and waited for the nuclear explosion. There was a silence of about ten seconds and then he burst into laughter.

'Well that's nothing to worry about; soon get over that.'

'I don't see how.'

'Just listen to this.'

Whereupon he telephoned the Architect and explained that his diligent young member of staff had accidentally slipped up and, in the rush of trying to get the job done on time, had forgotten to tell the Glazier to substitute rough-cast, plate-glass windows for sand-blasted, polished plate.

'Can you help him out?'

'Yes, sure. Tell him not to worry about it. I'll cancel the variation order. He'll do worse things than that before he dies!'

And I suppose I have. I have certainly seen worse things happen and perhaps been more tolerant of them as a result of this episode. Whether or not the Client who footed the bill for the extra cost would have been tolerant is perhaps another matter. I doubt he ever found out about it, just as Clients very often never find out about the errors their Architects make involving extra work on site for which the Contractor has to be paid – out of the Client's pocket.

31

And the Dish Ran Away with the Spoon

There are various things a Contractor can do to prevent the Clerk of Works seeing something he does not want him to see. If the Clerk of Works is not resident on the site full-time there is no problem anyway; but it is not too difficult to divert the attention of the full-time inspector. An extended tea break might be sufficient, otherwise an extended lunch from time to time. If that is not practicable, clandestine alterations or the covering up of cock-ups can be carried out after hours when the Clerk of Works has departed.

Obviously this is fairly straightforward but on one job such items were generally attended to on a Wednesday afternoon. That was when the Clerk of Works, with the full cooperation of the Contractor and generally at his expense, had a 'bird' in. Every Wednesday afternoon the windows of his site hut were papered over with drawings and at about two o'clock a young lady – not necessarily the same one every time – would appear. She and the Clerk of Works would be ensconced until about four o'clock when she would depart thus providing two solid hours for any 'undercover' jobs to be completed.

On another job the Clerk of Works' paramour was actually resident on the site – quite by accident, not by design. But more than a few problems ensued as a result.

The project was a large one warranting a large canteen being set up on the site. The Clerk of Works took up residence shortly after the job started and within a month or so the canteen was large enough to justify a resident Manageress. In this particular case the Manageress was resident in the literal sense. She was used to dealing with large construction projects and travelled around in her own quite luxurious caravan, which was parked on the site. Her name was May.

May was very popular on the sites. She was an excellent cook and served up some cracking meals. Her canteen was undoubtedly one of the best I have come across over the years. And talking of coming across, that was not the only reason she was popular. Although she was in her early forties she was still quite an attractive dish herself – slim, shapely 5'3" tall, she had no difficulty at all in communicating with the men on the site, either verbally or bodily. She could out-swear the most verbose navvy.

All the staff were kept very busy and some of us were regularly on site until 7.30 or 8.00 pm most evenings. Between 5.30 and 6.00 pm we could get a scrumptious evening meal before the canteen closed at about 6.15 pm. It didn't escape my notice that from time to time the groundworks Foreman used to pay May's caravan a call at around 6.45 pm; and occasionally the Foreman Fitter – the senior mechanic - did likewise.

But the most significant caller was the Clerk of Works. After a few weeks he called on May on most evenings and apparently at weekends as well. Presumably she quite fancied him too – he was moderately good-looking – and May regarded a clean pair of hands as an improvement on her other two suitors.

Most of the operatives on the job were directly employed and as the work progressed their numbers increased. The administrative staff on the site increased in tandem. One day a new wages clerk, Terry Spooner, arrived on the site. It transpired that three or four years earlier Terry had worked on a previous site where May had managed the canteen. Terry and May had become somewhat more than 'just good friends'. All this was unbeknown to the present site management when Terry set out to carry on where he had left off before.

The Clerk of Works was not a happy man! Whenever he arrived at May's caravan Terry was there. If he got there first Terry arrived to interrupt; and since Terry was in lodgings and had no home to go to he could easily out-stay the Clerk of Works. The Clerk's mood became darker. He hardly spoke to anyone. More importantly he started querying the hours on Daywork sheets and refusing to sign them. Even worse he started going round the site condemning work. Nobody divined what the matter was.

One morning my young trainee assistant went out on the site and bumped into the Clerk of Works. They got chatting. Perhaps for want of someone to talk to, the Clerk came out with a few choice words about Terry and May. My trainee could not understand why the Clerk of Works should be upset with a Wages Clerk and the Canteen Manageress but during some bawdy office chat joked that maybe both Terry and the Clerk fancied May at the same time. I had heard that there were problems on the site.

'Hell, you might have hit the nail on the head,' I said and proceeded to buttonhole the Project Manager.

At first he was disbelieving when I mooted the theory. Then he thought about it. 'I know what we'll do, we'll transfer Terry Spooner to another job and see what happens.'

Terry didn't want to go, but when he said, 'It's that bloody Clerk of Works isn't it?' we knew we were on the right track. Nevertheless, we had to assure Terry, hand on heart, that the transfer was only for a week or two before he agreed to go with a good grace. He never came back though because I arranged for my trainee to drop the word to the Clerk of Works that Terry Spooner had gone for good.

Almost like magic things were back to normal – which proves the worth of a good dish! And of course if we wanted the Clerk of Works out of the way for an hour or two ...

32

Humour

An incident I saw in London some years ago illustrates just how the perception of humour can vary from person to person. At the time it seemed hilariously funny to me, as it has to some people I've related it to. Others have thought it quite nondescript. See what you think.

I was travelling up an escalator in one of London's tube stations, where the walls were lined with small advertisements in frames about 450 mm × 600 mm (18″ x 24″). At one time they seemed to advertise mainly items of ladies lingerie. Nowadays the subject matter seems to be principally about shows and attractions or maybe Aids or pregnancy testing. The metal frames containing the adverts are glass fronted and hinged, requiring a screwdriver or special key to open them. From time to time the advertisement cards have to be changed. As I went up the escalator on one side a man on the other side was opening one of the frames next to the down escalator, taking out the advert, replacing it with a new one and rescrewing or relocking the frame. All the time he was doing this the escalator was going down and, in order to remain in one position his legs were walking up! Nobody took any notice except me. I laughed out loud! There he was, stationary in relation to the wall whilst the lower half of his body continuously walked up stairs, subconsciously and apparently without effort.

*

Whether or not some of the happenings on construction sites would amuse you will also depend on your individual sense of humour. Again, what might be incredibly funny to one person might be completely unfunny to another. Not only is a sense of humour individual to each particular person – although obviously one thing might be seen as funny by many people – relating the sequence of a supposedly humorous event is also an individual talent. Some people are good at telling jokes, others are not. A professional comedian will tell you it is all in the timing. But it is not just that; the listener has to be in the right mood. Even a professional comedian likes to have a supporting act or a warm-up man.

In addition, some humour is male or female orientated or nationalistic. What is seen as funny in one country may not raise a titter in another. Even some words have quite different meanings. For example, a 'tramp' in England might be a 'bum' in America. An English 'bum', on the other hand, would probably be a 'toosh' or more likely 'fanny' in America – the latter 180 degrees different on this side of the Atlantic! In England what are generally referred to as 'bumbags' are 'fanny packs' in the USA. What an American would get if he went into an English shop and asked for a fanny pack I dread to think.

Some years ago my niece, visiting England from California for the first time in 20 years, landed in Ireland en route. Wanting to get her blonde hair retouched, she solemnly asked the receptionist of the hotel where she could get a touch-up!

Mind you it isn't necessary to impart the phraseology to produce the ambiguity. 'Where can I get felt?' was the question the young secretary was asking various members of the technical staff. Well there was no shortage of volunteers but she had considerable difficulty in getting the information she was after which quite simply was the name of a merchant who sold roofing felt. Her husband wanted to re-roof their garden shed.

*

137

On one occasion when I was a junior Surveyor I was called into my chief's office for some reason. He had chosen an unfortunate moment because I was practically hysterical with laughter. With some difficulty I managed to explain to him why.

His office was on the first floor. Along the corridor a few doors away a kindly middle-aged but rather staid spinster worked as a secretary. She often used to 'chat up' the junior members of staff. It so happened that on this particular day she had been instructed to move her office to a room on the ground floor. She duly solicited the assistance of two other juniors to move the shell of her desk and her chair. I happened to be passing; she called me over and in all seriousness asked me if I would take her drawers down. It was at that moment that I was summoned over the loudspeaker system to my chief's office. Fortunately he also had a good sense of humour.

*

It was many years later when, as a Site Agent, my sense of humour was not appreciated by the Architect. He came into my site office in a terrible temper and announced that he had torn his trousers. I smiled, which didn't help matters. Then I realised that I could not actually see any tear. 'Where?' I asked.

'On the bloody 5th floor!'

33

The Cat and the Fiddle

There are numerous opportunities for fiddles on construction sites. Obviously there are no statistics on the subject and, if there were, they would only record the unsuccessful fiddles.

The greatest scope for dishonesty is in connection with materials and Subcontractors. In a parallel category to materials I would include plant, that is equipment or machinery on hire. All materials and plant delivered to a site have to be signed for, the signature confirming receipt. Thus once the Site Checker has signed for a ten tonne load of sand the Contractor is contractually bound to pay for it. Such materials are sometimes supplied by volume and sometimes by weight. If they are supplied by volume it is the Checker's job to ensure that the delivering wagon is full to the brim. If the wagon has been loaded with the material 'heaped', the Checker can either level it off or use his judgement as to whether or not the load is full. Most Suppliers are honest I think, but any Supplier who can regularly supply loads merely 5 per cent short will make a lot of extra profit. If the Checker is only slightly 'bent' the Supplier can ensure that his wagons are not subject to too close a scrutiny simply by occasionally giving the checker a 'drink', that is a small monetary 'bonus'.

If a material such as sand is supplied by weight, the delivery ticket would be accompanied by, or comprise, a weighbridge record. The lorry would either be weighed on a public weigh-bridge before arriving at the site, or on a very large site the

Contractor would install his own weighbridge. This would have to be officially certified as accurate to prevent the Contractor fiddling the Supplier!

At first sight, weighing the material appears to be more accurate and less prone to fiddling than where material is supplied by volume. This is not necessarily so. The first precaution that has to be taken is to ensure that the driver of the lorry gets out of his cab when the loaded lorry is weighed, otherwise the Contractor ends up paying for weight of the driver! The next precaution is to ensure that water has not been poured into a material such as sand before it is weighed. We have all seen loaded wagons leaving a trail of water on the road as they go to a construction site.

The actual weight of material is calculated by deducting from the weight stated on the weighbridge ticket – the combined weight of the lorry and the material – the tare or unloaded weight, which is always painted on the side of the vehicle. Any prudent Contractor will, at random intervals, insist that Suppliers' wagons return to the weighbridge after discharging their loads to verify the tare weight stated. Obviously if the tare weight is understated the Supplier is being overpaid for every load he delivers.

On a large construction site it is necessary to ensure that a lorry containing materials actually discharges the materials on the site. It is not unknown for a vehicle to enter the site, obtain a signature for the materials, leave by another gate and return a half an hour or so later with the same load of materials still on board. Thus it is necessary for the material to be inspected as the lorry arrives and for the empty vehicle to be inspected as it leaves the site. Only then should the delivery ticket be signed. Even so, it may be necessary for some additional precaution to be taken to ensure that the lorry has not left the site between the two inspections, when a part or all of the load could have been discharged elsewhere.

There is a ready demand for various types of building material in comparatively small quantities for sale cash-in-hand no questions asked. Small sites, self-employed gangs moonlighting, even the do-it-yourself enthusiast building his own garage, house extension or garden wall provide a market for bricks, sand, mortar or concrete.

Most Contractors buy liquid concrete factory-mixed these days. Ready-mixed concrete, as it is called, comes in large mobile mixers that have a capacity of about 7 cubic yards (5·5 cubic metres). Depending on the mix, each load will be worth at least £400–£500. One or two cubic yards will go quite a long way on a small job but would scarcely be missed on a large job.

There is always a certain amount of quite legitimate wastage of materials and it is never possible to check precisely how much should have been purchased for any given section of completed work. Nevertheless, I used to make quite detailed and meticulous checks and balances of various materials and on numerous occasions found discrepancies in bricks, mortar or concrete.

I was highly suspicious on one occasion when the General Foreman came to me one morning and said, 'I suppose I'd better tell you that we goofed yesterday afternoon.'

'What happened?'

'Two of us ordered seven yards of concrete for the same job. I ordered it for half past four, Bill ordered for quarter to five. We were halfway through placing the first load when the second load arrived.'

'So, what did you do?'

'Well, we couldn't send it back.'

'So, what did you do with it?'

'We buried it.'

'What do you mean you buried it?'

'We dug a hole with the JCB and buried it. I thought I'd better tell you because your measures won't tie up.'

My suspicion was that someone was doing a job on the side. But what could I do? I had no firm evidence and if the duplication was a genuine mistake I did not want to risk anybody being sacked by voicing my suspicions, which if groundless would have been disastrous. I took the easy way out and kept my suspicions to myself.

*

Sometimes 'material' has to be taken off site. The material might simply be rubbish or debris that has accrued from the works, or it might be excavated earth or 'muck' that has to be disposed of. Often a Haulage Contractor will be employed to cart the 'muck away' off the site and to a tip. As with new materials delivered, so with muck away – a ticket for each load has to be signed as each wagon leaves the site. And similarly it is necessary to ensure that a loaded wagon cannot just drive round for a few minutes and re-enter the site by another entrance.

When organising the work it is necessary to gear the number of lorries carting the muck to the number of machine excavators. Thus if there is only one excavator and it takes ten minutes to load each lorry, and the round trip from the site to the tip and back is one hour, then six lorries will be required. Fewer than six and the excavator will be standing idle part of the time; more than six and a queue of lorries will build up. At least that is the theory. In practice it rarely works out to perfection and if there is too much queueing the Haulage Contractor will complain. To appease him a few extra loads get signed for.

It is a small step from that to having a 'phantom' lorry operating all day or even all week, which was what happened on one occasion. One of my assistants recorded the numbers of all the lorries coming into and leaving the site transporting muck away. Nevertheless, when the invoices came in an extra wagon was recorded. I mentioned it to the Project Manager who reacted quite coolly. 'You just get on with measuring the job, eh. Leave doing it to us!'

He was obviously in on the scam. And since his boss was not noted for his honesty either there seemed little point in pursuing the matter. Talk about on the Hey Diddle Diddle!

*

142

Lorries, in common with other mechanical plant, may be hired on a time basis. This means that at the end of each day or week someone has to sign a time sheet certifying the hours worked. I do not need to describe the opportunities this presents for anyone so inclined to make a dishonest pound or two fiddling the times.

On one job more than the times were fiddled! We had a large Caterpillar tractor machine on hire, which because of the manufacturer's name, was generally referred to as 'the CAT'. The time came for it to go off site and arrangements were made for it to be collected. A wagon with a long, low-loading trailer was required and duly arrived at about three o'clock.

'You're a bit early.'

'Yes, well, no other jobs today.'

It took a quarter of an hour or so to load the tractor, the papers were signed and it was away. Half an hour later another low-loader arrived.

'We've come to collect the CAT.'

'It's already been collected.'

'Don't say they've doubled up on the wagon.'

They hadn't. The first low-loader carried the villains. It also carried the CAT into oblivion. Talk about the Cat and the fiddle!

34

If I Only had Wings

The current practice of power-floating the surface of concrete floors is done to achieve a smooth and – hopefully – level surface. If laid sufficiently accurately, it will receive thin tile or sheet finishings or carpeting without the need to lay a fine mixture of cement and sand as a screed on top. Nowadays, with computers and other equipment requiring a large amount of wiring, raised metallic or plastic floors are often installed on top of the concrete slabs. The sections of the raised floors are fitted with adjustable screw jacks, enabling them to be accurately levelled to receive the equipment and carpet or other finishes. Thus no cement and sand screed is required; indeed it may not even be necessary to power-float the concrete.

Sometimes the cement and sand screeds are still required, although not as frequently. Before the advent of the raised floors, the cement and sand screeds were often laid of sufficient thickness to accommodate services such as pipework to heating radiators or conduit tubing containing electrical wiring. To take these services, the screeds would be normally 35–50 mm (1½″–2″) in thickness. I say 'normally' because that would be the theoretical thickness required if the concrete slabs were laid level.

In practice it is not possible to lay concrete truly level. Even power-floated slabs undulate within certain tolerances. Indeed, even where cement and sand screeds are laid they will not be absolutely level. The surfaces of rough-tamped concrete will undulate to larger tolerances than power-floated slabs, but the levels of the surfaces of all types of concrete slabs will be affected by the accuracy of the temporary falsework or shutters on to which they are poured.

Various proprietary and other systems of shuttering are in common use. All have to be erected to the correct levels provided or checked by the site Engineer. Any error on his part will result in the floor being constructed at the wrong level. In addition, most shuttering systems deflect to a greater or lesser degree under the weight of the concrete when it is poured. The Engineer will attempt to anticipate this deflection when he checks the shutter level beforehand, or perhaps adjust the levels whilst the concrete is being poured. However, it is virtually an impossibility to set the levels absolutely right – hence the need for tolerances.

When a cement and sand screed is laid on the concrete slab the aim will be to lay it to the correct finished floor level, allowing only for the thickness of carpeting, tiling or other finish still to be laid. Clearly wherever the concrete slab is laid too low the screed has to be thickened to compensate. If the slab is too high the screed could be thinned down to compensate, but only if any buried pipework can still be accommodated. Otherwise it might be necessary to shave off the top of the concrete if the Structural Engineer will allow it. This would be a very expensive operation although less so than the alternative of relaying the concrete if the Structural Engineer will not permit the 'shaving off'.

Of the twin evils of laying the concrete high or low, the lesser one in these circumstances is low, since it is better to thicken the screed than risk having to cut or relay the concrete. Thickening the screed involves extra cost and might also incur objections from the Structural Engineer due to the extra weight of the screed material. Assuming he did not object, the extra cost would devolve to the Subcontractor whose job it is to lay the screed. He would want to recover the cost. Understandably he is generally not interested in being paid the 'nominal' thickness everywhere. This was my novel proposal to him when I was Project Surveyor.

145

He usually rejected it out of hand assuring me that he would let me know whenever the nominal thickness was exceeded. It is amazing how floor screed layers and plasterers (the work is usually carried out by the same firm) look at thickness through 'one-way' glasses. The only see the thick bits!

Being keen and enthusiastic in my younger days I used to keep a detailed record of the floor screed thicknesses. This I achieved by going round the site last thing before I left each day. Screeds laid in the early part of the day were by then hard enough to walk on but still 'green' enough either to push my measuring rod into them or tap a nail into. Those that were too soft to walk on I checked first thing the following morning. I kept a meticulous record of the thickness marked up on a layout plan to the chagrin of the Subcontractor.

On one occasion during my later afternoon tour of the site I was busy recording the thicknesses of a large area of screed laid that day. I was in the centre of the area, all of which was moderately hard, when my feet started to sink. The screed was quite thick and I suppose that although the surface was hard, the material was still soft underneath.

It made no difference in which direction I moved – my feet sank. In the end I left a trail of footprints which began in the centre and led outwards in several directions. It looked as though I had been dropped in the middle by helicopter. What the floor layer said the next morning was probably unprintable.

*

One of the floors in the same building turned out to be 50 mm (2″) lower than it should have been. The error was probably caused by the site Engineer misreading the level staff by a couple of notches when the shuttering was being set up. A simple human error, but the consequences were far-reaching and very expensive. From what I have said above, you will appreciate that the floor screed, which was supposed to be a nominal 50 mm (2″) in thickness, had to be made up to 100 mm (4″) to compensate for the mistake. An extra 50 mm of screed provided a lot of extra superimposed weight on the floor and it was only with a lot of persuasion that the Structural Engineer agreed that his original calculations were rather pessimistic and that his calculated margin of safety would accommodate the extra weight.

The cost of the extra 50 mm of screed was considerable, but that came along towards the end of the job. Before that, two other major problems had to be surmounted. Around the perimeter of each floor slab there was a continuous beam of what is called the 'downstand' variety; that is it projected below the underside of the floor slab to provide a head to the many window openings on the floor beneath. That continuous beam, and consequently all the window heads, were therefore also 50 mm too low.

Initially it was not thought to be a problem because if the windows were installed 50 mm low, the cills could easily be lowered by the same amount. Unfortunately the cills were quite low in height in the first place, and the dwarf brick walls under the cills were there primarily to screen and support the heating radiators. The dwarf walls could not be reduced in height because the cill heights were fixed; the only alternative was to reduce the height of all the windows.

Although the windows were of an expensive material and of a complex design, reducing the heights would have presented no great problem – except for one thing. Getting metal windows made and delivered on time was always difficult. They invariably arrived late – except when Sod's Law operated as it did with unerring certainty on this occasion. The windows were already on site! There was nothing for it but to send all the ones required for the floor concerned back to the works to be altered at great expense.

The great expense did not end there. If the building had been faced in brickwork, any alteration in height could have been accommodated by a bit of juggling around involving the cutting of a few facing bricks, but this building was clad in stone. Every dividing column between every window had to be reduced in height. To cut one course of stone to each column would have stood out like the proverbial sore thumb. The courses had to be reduced equally and the cost was enormous. Did heads roll? I honestly can't remember.

*

The stonemason probably had a special chuckle to himself when he was asked to cooperate in cutting down all these stones because a few weeks earlier he had incurred the General Foreman's wrath more than somewhat.

As was quite normal, the stonemason was provided with a certain amount of 'attendance' by the Main Contractor. This was a contractual obligation and it required the Contractor to assist with the unloading, hoisting and distribution of masonry items when they were delivered. The Contractor's tower crane was utilised for this purpose. The problem that usually arises in that circumstance is that the tower crane is used for a variety of purposes. Numerous Subcontractors might be entitled to have assistance with unloading. When they know there is a tower crane available they will take advantage of the fact by delivering their materials in larger packages or crates than might otherwise be the case.

With cooperation and prearrangement this can usually be accommodated but the Subcontractors often just arrange for their materials to arrive and hope for the best. 'The best' might be achieved by dropping a 'sweetener' to the key man involved. On this occasion the stonemason mistakenly thought the key man was the crane driver. For a regular weekly 'bonus' he had arranged that whenever a load of stone arrived, the crane would immediately unload it, deferring whatever else it was doing for the time being.

After a week or two the General Foreman caught on to what was happening and rapidly and forcefully amended the arrangements. 'On this job I say what the bloody crane does, and *I* say when it does it. And by the way, if there's any 'incentive' payments going, *I'm* the one to give 'em to!'

*

That General Foreman had things well organised as I realised some time later when he told me – in a friendly way – to mind my own business.

'Assisting with unloading and distributing materials' can cover a variety of things and sometimes the definition is not too precise. So whilst unloading is fairly straightforward, it is debatable exactly where distribution stops and the actual operation of fixing or installing begins. In many cases distribution will be defined as taking the Subcontractor's materials to his store or compound. From then on, handling them is part of the Subcontractor's job. On a multi-storey job distribution may be defined as 'depositing the materials at an agreed point on each floor level'.

On this particular job the General Foreman solved matters by 'giving' about ten or fifteen of his men to the Subcontractor who was installing the central heating system. I found that the Subcontractor was using them, not just to distribute his materials right to the actual point of fixing, not just to cut any holes that he required through the structure – which was quite probably something the Main Contractor was required to do – but to carry out every bit of unskilled work included in his installation. Heating fitters, like plumbers, often work in pairs – one skilled, one a mate. I found that all the 'mates' were employees of my Firm, the Main Contractor.

When I delicately raised the matter with the General Foreman his reaction was on the lines of, 'Never you mind about that. You just see to your ****ing job and I'll organise the ****ing labour!'

149

35

Who, Me?

It is surprising how cooperative an Architect can be in overcoming the effects of a mistake if the reason for it emanates from the Architect's own office. I have known instances where walls have been built in the wrong place – perhaps a hundred millimetres or so out of position. 'No,' said the Architect, 'it'll have to come down.' Quite reasonably he pointed out it would make a corridor too wide/narrow, or a room asymetrical. Then it was found that the error devolved from a wrong dimension on the layout drawing. Suddenly the impossible became possible, the impracticable quite simple, the 'out of the question' 'worth considering'.

Occasionally Architects discover their mistakes before the Contractor does. Most Contractors will do their best to overcome the errors at minimal cost, sometimes even at no cost at all to the Client. After all, if the Contractor gets the Architect out of trouble the Architect is under an obligation to him. Discharging that obligation may or may not cost the Client, or some other Client, some money – then or at some other time – but at least the working atmosphere remains friendly – for the time being.

Nevertheless, there are those Architects who will try to conceal their mistakes or even blame them on the Contractor. One rather naughty little dodge is the concealed revision.

On many jobs there are numerous design changes, sometimes major, but often quite minor. These manifest themselves in the issue of revised drawings which are usually designated with a revision letter. Thus drawing number 101 becomes drawing 101A, 101B and so on as the revisions occur. Sometimes they go right through the alphabet and drawing number 101AA will be issued.

Generally the revisions are listed on the drawing itself with a brief note of what was involved. Some Architects outline or highlight the revision in the body of the drawing to make it easy to find. Others – the villains – will make, say, three amendments under revision M but will list or highlight only two of them. The third is the 'concealed revision', which goes unnoticed and probably revises something already built. When the error is found on the site the Contractor will check back to the drawing and may well fail to realise that he built the work to an earlier version. On more than one occasion when I was based on site as a Project Surveyor I had to argue to convince the Contractor's Site Management that what they thought was their cock-up was in fact nothing of the kind. Unfortunately on many occasions they were right. Sometimes the mistakes beggared belief.

For example one job I dealt with was to build the extension to a hospital. It was not a large contract but included in the work was the construction of an incinerator in the grounds of the hospital to burn used rubbish dressings, perhaps amputated limbs and the like. It was a simple construction consisting of brickwork forming a chamber three or four metres square and about 1·5 metres high, with a concrete roof and a tall brick chimney. It had an iron door in the side to provide access.

A week or two after the job was completed I received a telephone call from the Architect to say that the hospital had reported that the incinerator would not work. I went to the site to investigate, although all I could think of as a possible explanation was that there were too few air vents provided to allow the requisite air inflow. All the vents seemed to be there; none were blocked. With some trepidation I opened the access door and crawled into the chamber to look up the chimney to see where the blockage was. Impossible. I could not look up the chimney because no hole had been left in the roof!

I could perhaps understand the concrete roof being poured without the opening for the flue – a simple enough omission; maybe the Ganger thought the hole was going to be chopped out later. But how on earth could the bricklayer who built the chimney have solemnly constructed it over a solid concrete slab? I couldn't believe it. Neither could my Boss when I reported back to him.

'Are you sure?'

'Yes.'

'It can't be true.'

'It is.'

'It's probably just a bit of concrete seepage that formed a thin skin on the underside of the roof.'

'No, I thought of that. I banged it with a hammer.'

There was nothing for it. At great expense we had to demolish the chimney, cut out part of the concrete roof and rebuild the chimney. An embarrassment to all concerned.

*

Most mistakes that occur on construction sites are probably the result of human error rather than – in the case of the incinerator – blatant stupidity. Simply misreading a measuring tape or an instrument can have serious after-effects, although in many cases the after-effects I have seen could have been avoided by cross-checking measurements or heights. The urgency to get the job done sometimes prompts 'shortcuts' which cause chaos.

I heard of one wing of a hotel where a floor was constructed one foot too high. Because of restrictions on the height of the building, it had to be demolished. Otherwise it would probably have been left.

I have seen a line of houses built, all equidistant apart. Between two of the houses there should have been a gap for a side turning. I left that Firm before I found out how they got over that one. (I hasten to say I was not responsible!)

152

I heard of an approach road to one site that was constructed literally in the wrong field. I did not know the details at the time but I believe some extra land was purchased to accommodate the error, that being cheaper than reconstructing the road.

*

On one housing site I was connected with, one four-bedroomed, detached house was built with the floor–ceiling height on the first floor measuring 2·1 metres instead of 2·4 metres. In Imperial measurement terms it was less than 7 feet high. The Clerk of Works, a very friendly and helpful chap, found the error on his final inspection prior to the handover on completion The poor fellow was quite apologetic when he explained that he just couldn't accept it!

Even that disaster was overcome comparatively economically. Over a weekend the first floor was supported with steel props whilst the whole of the tiled roof was jacked up 300 mm (1 foot), all the external walls and internal partitions were raised by the same amount and the roof reset to the correct level. All that remained after the weekend was to plaster and decorate the new sections of wall and amend the rainwater pipes. When it was completed you 'couldn't see the join'.

36

Get Ready ... Fire!

Site progress meetings vary in their degree of formality – or informality. In most cases they are moderately informal, with the participants addressing one another by their first names. Sometimes, however, they can be quite formal affairs depending on the person in the chair. I have found, when I have chaired such meetings, that an informal atmosphere is more conducive to cooperation and puts people more at their ease.

Nevertheless, there are those who seem to feel that being in the chair somehow confers upon them an aura of godliness or superiority. They insist on being referred to by their surname 'Mr So-and-so' or 'Mr Chairman' or 'Chair'. Of course the whole effect is lost when something goes wrong, such as the incident when half a dozen cups of tea were upset, which I have already related.

Some Contractors try to give the appearance of formality for site meetings on large sites by providing an actual meeting room fitted out with half-decent table and chairs. This had an unfortunate consequence on one job where the chairs which were provided, whilst they had an expensive look about them, had been purchased rather cheaply from a second-hand furniture dealer. The Architect who was in the chair was the 'formal variety'. When he referred to the Contractor he spoke of him as 'my Contractor', an epithet not welcomed either by the Contractor himself or by the Client.

The Client's Quantity Surveyor – the PQS – was represented by a rather heavily built fellow. He duly took his place around the table but, some ten minutes after the meeting had got under way with due formality, he suddenly vanished below the table as his chair disintegrated under him. It is difficult to retain an air of formality in those circumstances.

Matters weren't helped generally when precisely the same thing happened again at the next site meeting. On the principle that 'lightning doesn't strike twice…' there were faint stirrings of a suggestion that someone had deliberately sabotaged the chair.

*

At one 'formal' site meeting, although the job was quite a small one, the Architect in the chair was the senior partner of his Firm. He brought with him one of his assistants, who he referred to as Hamish. The Managing Director and another Director of my firm also attended, so the total attendance was somewhat over the top to put it mildly. The mode of address was also over the top since my Managing Director habitually called everyone by their surname, whilst he insisted on being addressed as 'Sir' by his employees. He addressed the senior Architect as Smith and expected to be addressed as Jones in return. He also addressed the assistant Architect as Hamish, believing that to be his surname. However, he would have expected Hamish to have addressed him either as 'Sir' or 'Mr Jones'. Hamish was clearly unhappy at being addressed on first-name terms by 'The Contractor'. Noticing this, our junior Director whispered rather loudly to the MD 'Stop calling him Hamish – that's what his mum calls him!'

*

Site meetings can get a bit heavy if and when things start to go wrong out on site. The monies expended on a construction site are so large that with profit margins squeezed it does not take a great deal to go wrong to change what might be a profitable job into a loss-making one. Recriminations can begin very quickly.

The Contractor wants to recover any monies he has lost, if possible from the Client, but if not, then from anyone else who happens to be around – most probably a Subcontractor. If it is from the Client, then the Client, if he thinks he is not at fault, will want an explanation from his Contract Administrator and may well blame him. In short everyone will be looking to guard their rear.

So far as the Client is concerned, Subcontractors equate with the Main Contractor. In fact so far as any battle with the Client is concerned the Contractor and his Subcontractors are on the same side. Indeed as previously explained, some Main Contractors will not permit their Subcontractors to attend site meetings for fear of an argument developing between them to the detriment of both. This applies in particular to what are known as domestic Subcontractors, that is those Subcontractors who are appointed solely by the choice of the Main Contractor.

The situation was somewhat different in the case of those Subcontractors classified as Nominated Subcontractors. These Firms were specialists in such things as heating, air conditioning or lift installations, and they were actually selected by the Contract Administrator. In a sense were imposed on the Main Contractor. He could object to their appointment if he could produce really strong reasons for doing so, but in practice such objections were rare. However, it is evident that, once the appointment is made and the specialist firm becomes a Subcontractor, the Contract Administrator has a special interest in ensuring that the Firm concerned carries out the work properly. For this reason it was usual for Nominated Subcontractors to be represented at site meetings.

For similar reasons, it is becoming less prevalent for Contract Administrators to formally nominate specialist Firms. Nowadays there is a tendency for Administrators to name several specialists, leaving the final choice to the Main Contractor. In this way an Administrator can distance himself from the appointment and thus blame the Contractor if the specialist fails to come up to scratch.

157

Specialist firms often display one particular shortcoming: they act as if the project is designed round them, almost even for their benefit. Certainly they often seem to believe that the Contractor's programme should be orientated around their requirements, rather than the Client's. This is perhaps less the case in the conditions of recession.

As a site meeting progresses each specialist Subcontractor will be dealt with one by one. Any problems he is experiencing will be examined and if he is allegedly not performing properly his representative will be closely examined for an explanation. This examination can be quite formidable. On one site I dealt with it was almost like a Star Chamber, to the extent that each specialist Subcontractor, when his turn came, took his seat in a particular chair, just as a witness might do at an Arbitration hearing. Ranged in front of him was an array of inquisitors. The Client's representative was a high-powered, top executive who attended every site meeting. He arrived in a Rolls Royce. He was easily distinguished from everyone else by his Saville Row suit, complete with carnation buttonhole, bowler hat, umbrella and spats. Notwithstanding his dandy-like appearance, which drew some caustic comments from the navvies as he walked around the site, he knew what questions to ask and was empowered to make instant decisions on behalf of the Client. Thus it was always difficult to attribute any unfair blame to the Client for any delays or other shortcomings on the part of the Contractor or specialists. Also among the inquisitors was the Architect, the site Project Manager and his immediate senior, the Contractor's Contract Manager.

On one occasion a representative of a partitioning firm took his place in the hot seat. Blissfully unaware of what was coming, and blithely used to making delivery promises with complete disregard as to whether or not they could be fulfilled, he was asked why his Firm had failed to commence work a few days earlier as had been promised several weeks previously. Stumped for anything better to say, he said blandly, 'The site wasn't ready'.

The Contracts Manager, a burly Scot in his late sixties or early seventies entered the fray: 'What d'ya mean the site was ne ready?'

'Well, it wasn't ready, the floors weren't clear.'

'Which floors were ne clear?'

'Well, none of them.'

'What d'ye mean none of them? Have you been up to see?'

'Well, no but they never are.'

'These are. Have you spoken to the Site Agent about it?'

'No.'

The Client's Dandy intervened: 'If your Firm wants future orders to fit out any of our projects you'd better get your people started work on this site by tomorrow afternoon at the latest.'

The Contracts Manager again: 'You just take a walk around the site right now laddie, then 'phone your office and come back in here in thirty minutes to confirm that your men or materials will be here tomorrow.'

He did, and they were!

37

There but for the Grace of God ...

In the opening chapter of this book I gave an outline of the staff who would generally be found on a construction site. I also mentioned the stress and heart-searching that goes into the completion of a project. I touched briefly on the initial problems that can arise – like getting the building in the right place, for example, or locating the various components together correctly in relation to one another.

The principal snag is that, notwithstanding the very sophisticated equipment in use, the basic job is still done by human beings, and human beings make mistakes, especially when they are under pressure or in a hurry. The sophisticated equipment helps to take away the drudgery, but if you press the wrong button you get even bigger and better wrong answers! You can dial direct from one side of the world to the other these days but you can still get a wrong number. I got someone in the Congo once – unintentionally I mean – and I got the same wrong number three times in succession on one occasion when I was telephoning a relative in California. I disturbed an irate fellow in Japan! 'Konichi-wa,' he positively barked into the 'phone at my third attempt. The fact that it was the middle of the night there didn't exactly help.

Getting the building in the right place is not as easy as it might sound. Indeed, even finding the right place can sometimes be a problem. 'Are we in the right field?' may sound like a standard joke but I've heard of buildings built on the wrong site; even an approach road being constructed on the site next door to the correct one. I can't claim personal first-hand knowledge of either of these two events, and doubtless the reports are enhanced by repetition, but in the case of the access road I was working for the Firm concerned when it happened, although – thankfully – I was not based on the actual site where it occurred. However, I have been based on sites where mistakes have occurred. Indeed it is probably true to say that errors in setting-out have taken place on almost all, if not all, of the sites I have ever been concerned with.

The setting-out – that is the locating of the building, road, bridge or whatever – is generally done by an Engineer, a Civil Engineer for example, even on a Building contract. Only on quite small jobs would the setting out be done by the Foreman.

The Architects – on a building contract – or the Engineer – on a civil engineering contract – generally provide the Contractor with the basic data such as base lines or survey points from which the Contractor can properly locate or set-out the structure. Even a minor error early on can have serious consequences and it is therefore not unusual, and certainly advisable, for the Contractor to ask the Architect or Engineer to verify the initial setting-out. Sometimes there is a contractual requirement that this should happen, which is just as well because Architects particularly, and perhaps understandably, are reluctant to get involved.

Once the initial setting-out is done, all future detailed setting-out is the responsibility of the Contractor in any event. That is to say columns, walls, floors, staircases etc. all have to be set in the right location on the plan and, of course at the right level! Again the setting-out is generally done by an Engineer; and once again comparatively small errors can have major consequences. However, the human psyche being what it is, whilst a certain amount of sympathy might be generated for the perpetrator of the mistake, stretching even to the extent of helping him cover it up, the reaction generally is one of mirth.

Quantity Surveyors in particular seem to find mistakes by Engineers hilariously funny. This is perhaps because if the

Surveyor makes a mistake he can generally rub it out; and if he can't he can probably conceal it with a fair chance that no one else will ever find out about it. However, the Engineer's mistake can result in a wall or column having to be demolished and rebuilt; or a concrete floor having to be broken and reconstructed. And *everybody* knows, from the humblest junior member of staff to the Managing Director himself, who Sod's Law decrees will probably visit the site at the crucial moment of demolition.

*

As illustrated previously on pages 60 and 61, main entrances to buildings seem to attracts cock-ups, perhaps by the very fact that they are main entrances and therefore so important that everyone tries that bit harder to get everything right; but once again Sod's Law rears its head.

There was a big panic on one job not because of a cock-up on it but because staff and plant were urgently required during a weekend on another job to put right a serious error. Two large concrete columns had been constructed either to the wrong size or in the wrong position or both. The two columns were situated one on either side of the ornamental front entrance doors and screen at street level. The problem was that the building was already constructed ten storeys high. No solution was available other than to demolish and reconstruct the columns that supported the whole weight of the structure above.

It was arranged that the large reinforced concrete beam, which spanned between the two columns – and which fortunately it was possible to extend by splicing in some large additional reinforcing rods – would be heavily shored up. The shoring supported the weight of the building whilst the two columns were demolished and correctly reconstructed. The whole operation was success-fully completed over one weekend apart, I presume, from the removal of the shoring, which would have had to stay in position for a week or two.

*

On another job it was the steel beam over the main entrance doors and glazed screen that caused the problem. The columns were in the right place and so for that matter was the beam, which did not carry a massive load. It supported the edge of the first floor and some load transmitted from above, plus the weight of a reinforced concrete balcony at first-floor level. The balcony ran the full width of the main entrance and projected 2·5–3 metres (8–10 feet) beyond the face of the building, in effect forming a small canopy over the external entrance steps.

The thickness of the reinforced concrete balcony varied. It was thinnest at its extremity, which was about 75 mm (3″), and being cantilevered the steel reinforcing rods were near the top of the concrete, whereas in a normal slab spanning between two walls or beams they would be located near the bottom. This is because in a normal slab it is the bottom of the slab which is stretched under load, but in a cantilevered slab it is the top. The steel rods are designed to resist the stretching or tension where the inherent property of the concrete is virtually useless. Concrete is very strong when compressed but is very weak in tension – hence the necessity for steel reinforcing rods.

I was wandering around the site one day a couple of weeks or so after the balcony had been constructed and noticed that seven or eight pallets of bricks had been placed on the concrete balcony. Since each pallet held about 500 bricks and each brick weighed about 2·25 kilos (5lbs), I didn't need a calculator or slide rule to work out that nearly 10 tons of bricks had been stacked there. Even I, as a mere Surveyor, could see that this had to be way over the load for which the balcony was designed.

I found the Section Foreman and – as diplomatically as possible – pointed out that the balcony slab must be near collapse and that someone could be killed.

'It's all right, you worry too much,' he said.

'But it's near collapse.'

'All right I'll have a look at it when I've got a minute.'

'Now?'

'Look, just you get on and measure the bloody job. Leave us to do it, all right?

'No.'

'I'll see to it when I've got a minute.'

Maybe the word 'killed' had its effect, for half an hour or so later four or five of the pallets of bricks had been lowered to the ground leaving just two or three on the balcony. Now it was only loaded to perhaps twice the designed load instead of about five times!

But this was not the end of the story. As I said, it was the steel beam supporting the balcony that caused the problem. As the building rose above it, it started to sag. I don't suppose the bricks, which had been temporarily stored on the balcony, had done any good but at the time they appeared to have done no harm. At any rate, it was several weeks later that the deflection in the beam was noticed and was drawn to the attention of the Structural Engineer who had designed it.

Horror of horrors, he found an error in his design calculations. The beam was not heavy enough to span the distance between the columns and carry the required load at the same time. There was nothing for it but to replace it with a heavier beam, which in turn meant demolishing and reconstructing the cantilevered balcony slab.

All hell broke loose when the slab was demolished when it became apparent for all to see that the reinforcing rods had been set near the bottom of the slab, instead of near the top. How the balcony had failed to collapse when the bricks were stacked on top of it was little short of a miracle. Even without the bricks the slab would theoretically have been near collapse.

Structural engineers are often criticised for over-designing structures, that is designing them to carry far more than a reasonable safety factor would require. In this instance, they could argue that they were justified. Four layers of supervision had failed to notice the error; the Steel-fixer Foreman, the Site Engineer supervising him, the General Foreman and our friend, the Clerk of Works.